For such a time as this

For such a time as this

Published by The Conrad Press in the United Kingdom 2020

Tel: +44(0)1227 472 874
www.theconradpress.com
info@theconradpress.com

ISBN 978-1-913567-19-4

Typesetting by: Charlotte Mouncey, www.bookstyle.co.uk

The Conrad Press logo was designed by Maria Priestley.

Printed and bound in Great Britain by Clays Ltd, Elcograf S.p.A.

For such a time as this

Pauline Dewberry

Courage does not always roar. Sometimes, it is
the quiet voice at the end of the day saying,
'I will try again tomorrow.'

Anonymous

For Tony, for the gift of life.
For Lawrence, who opened my heart
and taught me to love again.

Contents

Acknowledgements 11

Introduction 15

Chapter 1 – Alarming news 19

Chapter 2 – Can it get any worse? 29

Chapter 3 – Reality sets in 41

Chapter 4 – Life gets more scary 49

Chapter 5 – Fantastic news! 54

Chapter 6 – Things are beginning to happen 57

Chapter 7 – The chemotherapy journey begins – almost! 63

Chapter 8 – Finally it begins 71

Chapter 9 – Exit the Hickman Line 84

Chapter 10 – When can I go home? 89

Chapter 11 – Stem cell transplant time 95

Chapter 12 – And so it drags on 102

Chapter 13 – Are we nearly there yet? 111

Chapter 14 – Transplant time! 118

Chapter 15 – Remind me again, whose idea was it that
I should have stem cells ...? 125

Chapter 16 – A 'simple' virus? 132

Chapter 17 – CMV, MRSA and the flu! Really? 139

Chapter 18 – Signs of progress 146

Chapter 19 – January 2008 – Revelations and resolutions 154

Chapter 20 – Setbacks and disappointments 158

Chapter 21 – Shingles and shopping 164

Chapter 22 – Easter 2008 168

Chapter 23 – Lymphocytes and GVHD 171

Chapter 24 – Waiting-room friends 177

Chapter 25 – Chemical analysis 183

Chapter 26 – My own personal Goliath 187

Chapter 27 – Sunshine and smiles 191

Chapter 28 – Graft Versus Host Disease 199

Chapter 29 – Missing words 208

Chapter 30 – Autumnal love 215

Chapter 31 – Feline therapy 225

Chapter 32 – One thousand days 235

Chapter 33 – Reflections 239

Epilogue 243

Notes and glossary of terms: 249

More about Pauline 253

Acknowledgements

An extraordinary number of people accompanied me on this incredible journey. Some were very active and vociferous, while others sat quietly in the background. All were appreciated and valued for their contributions: whether it was during my leukaemia 'trip' or in the writing and editing stages of this book.

To God, for bringing me through this ordeal with my sense of humour intact (most of the time), with slightly less hair, and by the healing power of his love.

For editorial advice and help, my grateful thanks to the following folk:

Gerald Schiffhorst, Stuart MacFarlane, Linda Mitchell, Mary Gibson, Susan Eldred, Richard Gibney, Aida Marina, Susanne Haywood, Carol Turner, Penel Ashworth, Jim Willis, and Arlene Sphikas.

Grateful thanks to Marilyn Edwards, author of the Moon Cottage Cats books, for her wonderful support, friendship and helpful suggestions while writing this book.

Special thanks to Dale (Slim) Haines and Phil Wolfe, for their friendship; the wonderful chemo nurses – Keith, Linda and Yvonne, at Queen Mary's Hospital. Thanks, too, to the doctors and nurses on Gillies Ward, technicians, porters, Friends of the Hospital Refreshments Bar and transport staff at Queen Mary's Hospital, Sidcup, Kent, and at King's College Hospital, Denmark Hill, London, for all your skills, wisdom, kindness, sense of humour, and gifts of friendship.

To all my 'Waiting-room' Friends: Val, Phil, Mr Chung, Joy, Dennis, Jeni, Rita, Therese, Ron and Glenda, and many others. Especially to Larraine and Val, who allowed me to share their journeys as well as enriching mine as we met twice weekly for our blood tests.

To Geoff Clarke, the vicar of my church (Northumberland Heath Anglican Church), for getting the prayers up and running the same day that I found out I had leukaemia. Thank you for your continued prayer support and bless you for not minding about the funny tasting coffee and walnut sponge cake!

To my church family and all the wonderful ladies: Dorothy, Elaine, Margaret, Marion, Monica, Sue and Viv, who brought me a dinner every evening for months on end – thank you all.

To Del and Carol Barefoot and the members of their congregation at Wellspring Pentecostal Church, in Welling, Kent. Thank you for your ongoing prayers and the visits to see me in hospital.

To the fantastic subscribers of my website: www.thedailymews.com; thank you for not bailing when times got tough, and for the prayers, the letters of encouragement, the gifts, the emails and the phone calls. To Stacy Mantle and Jeff Shepherd who maintained and updated the website for me and sent out the Mewsletters – thank you both.

To the army (or so it seemed) of people who rallied round when I needed bits of shopping, or something: Jenny Goddard, Rosie, Gary Scott, Marge, and other friends and neighbours, especially Steve Carlisle who looked after my cats and the house while I was in hospital – thank you so much.

To the amazing people that run Leukaemia Care Charity, for their wonderful support and guidance when I couldn't cope with the negativity around me.

Special thanks to Garfield, Billy, Timmy, Sam, Ricky and Ollie – my beloved feline friends, whose purring engines kicked into gear as they lay alongside me on the sofa. Thank you, my little furry babies, the journey would have been a lot darker without you all being by my side, loving me better with your purr-atherapy!

To Almeric Johnson, once my boss and now a good friend, for all his 'boot up the bum' encouragement and motivation and helping me to believe in myself.

To my brother Tony, for sharing his stem cells and lymphocytes with me. If he hadn't had been a tissue match, you wouldn't be reading this book now.

To Adrian Magson, for all his patience, kindness, and encouragement in helping me believe I could do this.

To Aida Marina, who designed the most beautiful cover based on my ramblings and incoherent ideas!

To James Essinger at The Conrad Press for believing in me and taking a chance on an unknown.

And last, but certainly not least, to Lawrence, my soulmate, for being who you are and helping me to be the best me that I can be.

Introduction

Initially, I began to write this book as a kind of journal. As the weeks passed before the chemotherapy started, I wrote down events as they unfolded. I was trying to make sense of why I got leukaemia. Why me? Why had I been singled out to be the recipient of this particular disease? Was it some kind of test? Were God and the angels all watching from their vantage point in the clouds to see how I handled this next phase in my life? As tests go, it was pretty horrific, and I failed to see how I could pass it successfully.

I realised quite early in the journey that I needed to make sense of things, to verbalise my thoughts. In actually putting words down on paper it meant I was acknowledging my imperfections – I had a disease which might possibly kill me – so now I wasn't as perfect as I once thought. And by being perfect, I don't mean I thought more highly of myself. On the contrary, I probably had the world's biggest inferiority complex and I always struggled with low self-esteem. I meant that my body, which other than living with Chronic Fatigue Syndrome for a number of years, and a few operations on my lady bits, had done me surprisingly well.

In writing down the fears, worries, concerns, and other aspects of the whole situation, I found that there was some kind of cathartic exercise being played out. The consultants, both at the local hospital, Queen Mary's, Sidcup, Kent, and King's College Hospital, in Denmark Hill, London, had been unable to answer my questions about why and how I got leukaemia. I knew that some cancers are possibly caused by poor lifestyle choices, but I didn't smoke, didn't drink alcohol and had never touched recreational drugs.

I had heard about cellular memory. It's been suggested that the body, if it suffers a trauma of some kind, retains the memory and sometimes, (but not always), later in life, cancer can manifest. It doesn't seem to happen to everyone, but the books I have read on healing cellular memory focus on going back to the point of trauma, dealing with it, letting it pass peacefully from one's mind and, ultimately, healing the mind and body.

It all sounds far-fetched, I know, and some people may switch off at this point and think I'm a nutter - Ok, you're entitled to your opinion – but, as three of my cats all had different types of cancer, I looked into it a bit more. One of my cats, Ricky, had been the subject of a cruelty case. He'd been kept in a rabbit hutch for a year by his 'people' until the RSPCA had found him and removed him from the situation. I don't know what ever happened to his 'people', but he was taken to the Cats Protection where he languished in a pen for six months until I saw him in the classified ads in my local newspaper. It was love at first sight.

It took a long time, many months, before Ricky trusted me. If he climbed up on the sofa, he seemed to duck in readiness for a telling off. I never told him off because, in my opinion, he wasn't doing anything wrong. And over time, he began to behave like a cat who was allowed to be what he wanted to be – and to be able to live his life quietly and with dignity.

A year after my diagnosis, Ricky developed lymphoma of the

nasal passages. Chemotherapy is not really a viable treatment in cats because it makes them so ill it depresses them too much. And the success rate isn't very high. So, we made the difficult decision to put Ricky to sleep. Coming a year after losing my twenty-year-old cat, Garfield, it was very hard to deal with. It was only much later, though, having read the book on healing cellular memories that the idea came to me. Maybe Ricky had been traumatised by his early treatment and this had caused him to get cancer, especially as he had to spend four months in a cattery while I was gaining my strength after the transplant. It's possible that he remembered being in the rabbit hutch when he was a younger cat, and the cancer was brought on by anxiety.

My own life had been fraught with stressful situations: my parents' divorce when I was about eleven, a difficult relationship with my mother which at times seemed resolved, but other times seemed to go backwards again, my own divorce, and enforced house moves to new areas, and working in stressful environments – all these things could, perhaps, have contributed towards me getting leukaemia. The jury is still out on what causes cancer – certain cancers – in some people and in my quest to find answers, I came to my own conclusions, having carried out research online and reading numerous books on the subject.

The overriding thing, for me, in writing this book is I have learnt so much. I have learned about myself, my strengths, my weaknesses, and surprised myself. I've learned about the strengths and weaknesses of family members and friends, and been disappointed that some of the people I thought would be there for me, were not, while other people who, I never in a million years thought would care about me, stepped up to the plate, and went that extra mile.

I have learned that the human body is an amazing machine, but that the power of the mind is what carries a person through the most critical situations and circumstances. I've learned that having a positive mindset can often mean overcoming seemingly hopeless situations. And, of course, my faith. Having that unshakable faith that God would heal me in his own way, in his own time, was what kept me going through the dark days when it did look as if I might not make it after all.

In the end, the book became the means to survive. It had to be written because I overcame insurmountable odds, I beat the bully, and I am the victor. I needed to tell my story, not to make people feel sorry for me, but to realise that despite the odds being stacked up against you, it IS possible to look your enemy in the eye and win.

And the amazing thing about this entire journey was that not only did I find out what I was capable of, I also found myself, and who I am. And perhaps, even more incredible was that I met my soul mate. At the age of fifty-eight, overweight, bald, with perhaps a life-limiting illness, I met the man who would change my life for the better.

So why did I write this book? Because I wanted to share my incredible story with you and hope that you are inspired as you set out on your own journey. If life hands you lemons, you make lemonade.

Chapter 1 – Alarming news

Six months! six months in hospital! I looked at the consultant and wondered if, for a moment, I'd been transported into a parallel universe and was somehow taking part in a tacky TV reality show. 'And the winner is ... and you have won the disease of the year and part of your prize will be to spend the next six months in hospital, undergoing intensive, aggressive chemotherapy.'

I looked at the fat green hospital file now emblazoned with a yellow band, the words 'Haematology and Oncology patient' written in black lettering – a warning that the person the file referred to was now 'unclean'.

The consultant, Dr W, tried her best to convey the results of the numerous blood tests and bone marrow tests, but I sat in stupefied silence. I felt so well. How could I possibly have Acute Myeloid Leukaemia? How did I get it? Why did I get it? And was I going to die? If so, when?

A chemotherapy nurse sat alongside Dr W with her hands folded in her lap. She didn't look at me at all, but she was there to field off the myriad questions that a person in my position – newly diagnosed with a funny sounding disease – would obviously throw in her direction. But this articulate, intelligent, usually bright and positive woman had been struck dumb and I couldn't think of a single thing to ask.

Dr W continued to talk about percentages of blasts, platelet counts, white blood cell counts and other things which were all Greek to me. I didn't have clue what she was talking about, but the gentle tone in which she delivered this unwelcome visitor to my life made me feel that it was somehow going to be all right. That was, until she said, 'And you'll have to come into hospital within the next two weeks to have six months of intensive, aggressive chemotherapy.' That's when I found my voice; it came out louder than I meant it to, and we all jumped. Only then, perhaps, did I realise just how fierce I could be.

I think I half stood and put my hands up. 'SIX MONTHS!' I roared. 'SIX MONTHS! I can't spend six months in hospital; I'm a very busy woman.' They both smiled at me indulgently, but I wasn't joking. Who goes into hospital for six months? I had six cats waiting for me at home, the eldest of which, Garfield, was a beautiful ginger geriatric feline aged twenty. He had several health problems and needed twenty-four/seven care. I didn't know anyone who would or could interpret his meows the way I could. I couldn't leave him for six months, it would cause him untold anxiety, and probably hasten his death. If I couldn't be there for him – well, I didn't want to think about it.

No, I wasn't going into hospital for six months. I wasn't ill. I was sure they had made a mistake and that they had got the wrong person. It was one of those silly mix-ups where two patients have got the same name and, although that was most certainly my hospital file, the other Pauline Dewberry was the one, unfortunately, who had leukaemia. I was sorry for her but I wanted to get home to my cats and, eventually, I would tell my friends, have them in hysterics about the time the hospital got me mixed up with someone else, and how I nearly went into hospital to have chemotherapy. How we would laugh at yet another NHS blunder.

Dr W smiled. The chemotherapy nurse smiled. They both looked at me, but I wasn't smiling. This was for real. Suddenly, I felt myself sucked up out of my body towards the ceiling, and from my vantage point I could look down on the three people sitting below me, each one part of a tense, carefully orchestrated drama. I spent the rest of the consultation looking down from the ceiling, watching as this one act play worked itself out. It was a monologue as only one person was talking, Dr W, but I didn't hear or understand anything she said. There were three players, but one was fiddling with her fingers in her lap while the other one sat mute listening as her life unravelled in a foreign language.

It was a tiny office, almost like a cupboard, and three walls were lined with shelves; files, books, papers and endless paraphernalia relating to patients' lives were dotted on every surface. There was a small window, but the room seemed very claustrophobic and I felt hot and uncomfortable.

It was 7 June 2006 and in August I would be fifty-six years of age. I was a divorced woman, a bit overweight, well, all right then, more than a bit, and I hadn't worked for about twelve years because back in September 1994 my GP had signed me off work because I was too ill with Chronic Fatigue Syndrome.

I had two sons, and three grandchildren, and six cats. I was happy and content with my life and thought I would just work on my website, which is about cats, write articles now and then for publication, and write that book when I could find something to write about.

I had pretty much got my life summed up. There wasn't a Mister Right in the picture, but that was ok because I was busy with all my projects; I was a pet bereavement counsellor, a pet behaviourist majoring in cats, I was active in my local church and other churches in the area, and Garfield, my elderly geriatric senior Kitizen kept me busy with his needs. It was a bit like looking after one's granddad, only granddads don't usually pee in your slippers, but he was such a special cat, it was an honour and a privilege to take care of him. I had a reasonable social life where I met up with friends for coffee or lunch and I could honestly say I was happy with my lot.

Getting a cold in the early winter months was pretty much par for the course for me. Unfortunately, it didn't usually stop there. It was quite common for me to get a chest infection, followed by an ear infection and then, if I was really unlucky, a kidney infection. This is what had happened earlier in the year. When I'd seen one of the practice nurses at my doctor's surgery because I had the symptoms of a chest infection, she sent me for a routine blood test for my thyroid function, as I have an under-active thyroid. Sometimes, but not always, an underactive thyroid goes hand in hand with Chronic Fatigue Syndrome.

I was surprised when, a few days later, one of the doctors at the surgery rang me and asked how I was feeling. I told her that my chest didn't seem any better so she asked me if I could go to the surgery. She gave me more antibiotics and another blood test form. This happened three more times when, I'd go for a blood test, she'd ring me up and ask how I was feeling, after which she'd give me more antibiotics and another blood test form.

I had to wait four weeks after the last course of antibiotics were out of my system before having the final blood test. Once again, the doctor rang me and asked how I was feeling. I told her that I was feeling much better now, but she still wanted to see me.

She said that the Haematology Department at the local hospital in Sidcup, Kent, had some concerns over my test results, that my blasts were high, and my white blood cell count had been steadily dropping since February (when I had the first chest infection). She mentioned 'myelodysplasia' but, stupidly, I didn't ask what that was.

I had been volunteering at a local Citizen's Advice Bureau a couple of times a week and she suggested, that for the time being, I stopped working there because of the risk of infection. Once home, I Googled 'myelodysplasia'. Dozens of websites came up, all relating to leukaemia. Confused, I switched the computer off. I didn't have leukaemia. I was feeling well, and even the usual symptoms of Chronic Fatigue Syndrome weren't as bad as usual. I was convinced there'd been a huge mistake.

Back to my position on the ceiling, watching as Dr W outlined plans for treatment, I couldn't help wondering what was I supposed to do now with this intruder? How was I supposed to react? My friend Gary, a neighbour who lives across the road from me, had given me a lift to the hospital that morning and said he'd pick me up when I was ready to go home but I had never discussed anything of a personal nature with him. Who could I tell about this 'elephant in the room'? How would my friends and family members react when I finally told them? In just a few hours, I would find out when I made the first tentative phone calls.

And the bad news didn't end there. I had to have another bone marrow test that day as more sample material was needed for further tests to be carried out. I had to go back up to the ward where I had the first bone marrow test two weeks previously. This time, Dr W did it herself and she gave me plenty of sedation, so technically, I was 'knocked out' while she carried out the tests. Although I remember nothing of it, she said I wriggled and called out a few times. I didn't remember feeling anything, so the sedation had done its job. The first time I had it done it hurt like hell as the sedation is only meant as a relaxant, not an anaesthetic. To get the bone marrow material, the doctor drills down into the hip bone. This is done without anaesthetic, but the relaxant is meant to keep the patient calm. Depending on who carries out the task, it either hurts a lot or, if you're lucky, you don't feel much at all.

It was late afternoon when I was finally allowed to go home after the chemically induced zombiness had worn off and, true to his word, Gary came to collect me. In stupefied tones I told him the news – that I had this disease called 'Acute Myeloid Leukaemia'. 'F**k me!' was his only response. A tense graveyard silence engulfed the car on the journey home. As he dropped me off at my house, he kissed me on the cheek. A goodbye kiss? Would it be a last goodbye perhaps?

I went indoors and fed the six cats, five-year-old Ollie, nine-year-old Sam, ten-year-old brothers Billy and Timmy, thirteen-year-old Ricky, and Garfield who was twenty. Life had to go on as normal for them, as cats hate change to their routine. They like their meals at more or less the same time each day and so even though I had a million things to start organising, first things first - I had to prepare their dinners.

Dr W had told me that I would have to go into hospital on Monday 19 June, (which was in less than two weeks' time) to begin chemotherapy, so once I'd fed the cats, made myself a cappuccino, I hit the ground running. I rang up Geoff, the vicar of my church, to give him the news. As it was the first Wednesday in the month, there was a prayer and praise evening later at the church, and my news was put at the top of the agenda for divine intervention. I wouldn't now be able to attend because I had to start ringing around family and friends who were waiting to hear the results of all the tests I'd been having since February. I knew Geoff and the others would understand.

Meanwhile my main concern was how to break my awful news to my family members and my two sons; Paul aged thirty-six and David, aged thirty-four. How could I do this without frightening them? How could I do this without breaking down in tears? How could I do this without admitting to myself that I really was seriously ill and there was a very real chance that I wouldn't come through this?

Paul lived about a twenty-minute drive away. I rang him, asking if he could come over because I needed to tell him something urgently. David, and his wife, Tanya, were on holiday and wouldn't be home until the following week.

While waiting for Paul to arrive, I rang my friend, Steve, to see if he could call around the following morning after he'd finished his post round. Whenever I went on holiday, Steve stayed in my house to look after my cats and the house for me. I now needed his services for a bit longer than the usual fortnight – six months is a long time, but I needed to know that the cats were going to be looked after properly. The house needed to look 'lived in' so that burglars wouldn't chance their luck. That, and the ongoing care of my cats, was my prime concern.

I rang one of my close family members. 'Hi,' I began tentatively. 'Erm, I went to the hospital today and got the results of all those blood tests they've been doing for the past couple of months, and the bone marrow test they did a fortnight ago.'

There was no response from the other end of the phone. I carried on, taking a deep breath. 'You won't believe this,' I said, still scarcely believing it myself, 'but I've got something called Acute Myeloid Leukaemia, and I've got to go into hospital in less than two weeks' time for six months to have intensive, aggressive chemotherapy.'

The line clicked and went dead.

Stunned and deeply hurt, blinking back the tears, I stood with the phone still in my hand, wondering if everyone was going to hang up on me when I gave them the news. I needed the support – and love – of my family and judging by that first phone call, the love, and possibly the support, wasn't going to be there for me.

I couldn't believe that anyone would be so cruel to react in such a way. Even if the news isn't good, surely you don't put the phone down on someone without saying a word?

Despite that initial setback, the first few days were manic. People were coming and going as news filtered out, and various people from church began to offer to do things for me as and when the need arose. The phone didn't stop ringing and, in between receiving calls, I had to make dozens of them informing various other family members and friends of this latest development.

My consultant, Dr W, had mentioned that siblings have a one in four chance of being a donor bone marrow match, so I had to ask my two brothers if they would consider having a blood test to decide if they were a tissue match. As I'm over forty-five years of age, I was informed that a full bone marrow transplant is not viable. All that is done is a stem cell transplant, which is called a gentle option, and for this, the donor sits in a chair with a tube in both arms; one tube collects the blood and carries it to a machine something like a kidney dialysis machine, where the stem cells are harvested, together with other components of the blood which might be needed later, before sending the blood back through the tube in the other arm. It's painless and non-invasive, unlike a proper bone marrow operation – which would be excruciating if the test was anything to go by and would require a few days in hospital and several days off work afterwards to recover.

So, the first few days after the diagnosis were spent in frantic activity. Lists were drawn up of people to write to, to telephone, email. Still more lists contained items that I'd need to take into hospital with me, and more lists had items that I needed to buy so that the cats had enough food month by month, as I wouldn't be able to go shopping on the couple of days in between the monthly chemotherapy courses. I had been told that I might be allowed home at the end of each month's course so that I didn't go 'stir crazy', but I wouldn't be allowed out as I would be neutropenic and at risk from infections.

I had lists all over the table and, as I remembered something new, it was added to the relevant list and as I accomplished something, so it was crossed off. Then more lists were created in this almost military type exercise that I was adopting.

Despite telling people that I had leukaemia I, myself, still hadn't accepted the diagnosis. I looked extremely well. I didn't feel ill. To me it was almost as if I was living a lie and there were some people who didn't believe me when I told them that I had leukaemia. How could I possibly have something called Acute

Myeloid Leukaemia going on inside my body when I felt quite well? Even the symptoms of the Chronic Fatigue Syndrome had abated somewhat – perhaps in deference to an illness worthier of respect, but as I'd had CFS for over fourteen years it was a rare day when I was symptom free. For the first time in a very long time I could honestly say that I felt well. That was a strange thing in itself considering the blasts in my bone marrow were up to twenty percent and the white and red cell counts were low, and my platelets were doing their own thing.

If I thought receiving the news that I had Acute Myeloid Leukaemia was bad enough, a more upsetting situation was waiting in the wings to catch me off guard.

Chapter 2 – Can it get any worse?

The weekend of 10 June was a very sticky, hot one, and all the six cats wilted under their fur coats. Garfield, my beloved elderly cat, was having a particularly bad time with the heat.

With his various health problems, he'd been to the vets' several times in recent years. Just before his eighteenth birthday in March 2004 he was diagnosed with diabetes and I had to give him insulin injections twice a day.

I made sure that he had several small meals throughout the day to keep his glucose levels even and he managed to put on a little bit of weight. In the December of 2004 he had a seizure, which was insulin induced. His pancreas had suddenly started making insulin again and the little he received by way of injections had caused an overload – which resulted in him having the fit. At almost nineteen years of age – he had beaten diabetes, which our vet, Kevin, said was a miracle.

I prayed for all my cats every day and I regularly laid hands on Garfield while I prayed for him. I could often feel the heat through my palms warming that particular area of his body. Knowing God had answered my prayers, it was, indeed, a miracle that Garfield had been healed. I thought to myself if God could heal Garfield, surely, he could heal me?

But it was an unbearably hot weekend in June and Garfield was suffering. My office is in the back bedroom. Here, Garfield spent his days sleeping on a duvet, surrounded by pillows and his daytime teddies, Flump and Teddy. Timmy, who was almost ten, and his best friend in the world, usually lay alongside him, washing his face from time to time and just being a supporting presence. Garfield loved him and looked for him if he wasn't there.

I have a website on cats, called www.thedailymews.com and I had been updating it for a few days, and writing the Mewsletter which is sent out to all the subscribers. This gives links to all the new articles and other assorted items that I've put on the website. In addition to the usual cat items I wrote or added to the website, and mentioned in the Mewsletter, I now had to add the news about my health and impending six month stay in hospital. Fortunately, two Internet friends, Jeff in England and Stacy in the US, had agreed to continue the website for me, with Jeff putting content on the website while Stacy would send out the Mewsletter. I didn't know how long it would be before I could resume working on it and I didn't want it to remain static with no action or new content being added.

I kept looking round to check on Garfield to see if he was ok. I was surprised to find that most of the time he was awake and looking at me. Normally he would be asleep all the time, only waking up when he needed to go out in the garden or if he wanted some food.

'Garfield, do you want to tell Mummy something?' I asked him at one point, 'have you got anything you want to tell me?' He sighed a huge deep sigh and closed his eyes wearily.

I had already told Garfield that when he felt it was time to go, he would have to tell me because I knew I would be incapable of making that decision. I loved him so much it was going to be painful to let him go and, yet, that final act of love is to allow one's beloved pet to go on with dignity. I had had him and his brother, Biggles, since they were eight-week-old kittens and he was now twenty years and three months old, having beaten several serious health issues.

Most cats have an inner reserve of intelligence and wisdom. Garfield was incredibly wise and, over the years, had mentored most of the new feline additions to the family. To the other cats in my household, he was venerated for that vast well of knowledge. Life would be so different without his beautiful face and graceful personality in evidence every day and I knew the other cats, especially Timmy, would miss him dreadfully, not to mention the huge desperate aching loss I would feel.

I knew in my heart, that soon, I was probably going to have to make a hard decision, but I thought I would wait until the following day to see how he was faring, and whether, if it were cooler, he might be ok. However, looking at him the following morning, I was saddened to see that he could no longer stand up. I had spent most of the weekend trying to hold him up when he ate from his food bowl or drank from the water bowl he favoured in the lounge. When he went into the garden to go to the toilet, I had to not only hold him up, but also massage his abdomen to help him go. How long could he reasonably be expected to cope like that?

I rang the vet that morning to make a late afternoon appointment. I usually took my neighbour shopping on Monday mornings, and I knew if it were to be Garfield's last trip to the vet, that I'd be in no fit state to go shopping or do anything for the rest of the day. Trying to be as 'normal' as possible, my neighbour and I did our weekly shopping and I came home as quickly as I could so that I could spend more time with him.

I spent the last couple of hours with Garfield doing the things we would normally have done. He ate some dinner, went out in the garden and did a poo – which pleased me! It's funny how little things like that can bring a smile now because it meant that surely nothing was wrong. How I do seem to like living in this place called 'denial'.

I had taken more photos of him and all the cats over the weekend, some of which would be used on the website at some point in the future and then we had lots of cuddles and deep meaningful conversations as Garfield was a very vocal and affectionate cat.

At one point, he looked into my eyes as if he was trying to store and remember every part of my face. Tears escaped down my cheeks and with the gentlest of touches, he wiped them away with his paw. He continued to look at me, willing me to be strong and brave for what was to come, and I wondered, with his inherent feline wisdom, if he knew what was in store for me and was making life just that bit easier by leaving me now.

When Kevin, the vet, saw Garfield, he shook his head and said it was time. He examined him and said the reason why he was falling over so much was because he had no muscle tone in his back legs at all. I asked if I could hold him while it was done, and a towel was placed on my lap. I held Garfield in my arms and watched as Kevin clipped a bit of fur from his front paw. A vet nurse, a friend of mine, called Melanie, came in to help soothe Garfield, but he was pretty relaxed anyway, as I was talking to him as well – not looking now at what Kevin was doing.

I had my face close to Garfield as I told him how much I loved him, and how I would always love him. Then Garfield did a remarkable thing. He reached up and licked my face a few times which was his way of kissing me and then he was gone. It was all very peaceful, very dignified and I believe, it was what Garfield had been telling me the day before that he had had enough and was ready to join Biggles his brother, who had died nine years earlier in a tragic road accident.

Melanie rushed out of the room. I'm sure she was crying although she had to maintain a professional demeanour. Kevin kept swallowing hard while I blubbed like a baby, holding my beautiful Garfield in my arms and looking down at his peaceful lion-like face and still body. Everyone at the practice knew Garfield and loved him. When he was eighteen years old, just after he had been diagnosed with diabetes, he had to have some benign tumours in his mouth removed along with some rotten teeth. It was a big operation for a cat of his senior years and all the staff were on tenterhooks for Kevin, who was performing the operation, for me sitting waiting at home, and of course, for Garfield.

When I took him back a week later for his check-up, while Kevin was out the back emptying a dish that Garfield had obligingly done a wee in, Garfield walked through the door into the hub of the surgery. He went up to each member of staff in turn and meowed at them. They, in turn, responded with a 'hello, Garfield, how are you doing?' or something similar and in response he'd meow back at them. He went to everyone almost as if he was thanking each one of them personally for looking after him the previous week.

I brought him back home and laid him on a towel on the sofa. Each of the cats, Billy, Sam, Ricky and Ollie, came one by one to pay their respects, sniffing his face and giving me puzzled looks. Timmy sat alongside his best friend for several hours, occasionally washing his face and ears, before leaning over him in what might be a final feline kiss.

A friend came round and sat with me for a while; her twenty-year-old cat, Penny, had had to be put to sleep only a couple of weeks before Garfield. Cancer had sadly claimed her pretty little body. We each shared memories of our beautiful senior kitizens and all that they meant to us, and how life would not be the same again – despite both of us having other cats.

My heart was in shreds. I was still in denial about the leukaemia and now my best friend in the world, who had been with me through thick and thin for the past twenty years of my life, was no longer here to help me through this unknown horror that lay ahead.

I prayed for Timmy, because I knew he would mourn for his friend. Timmy had been Garfield's constant companion for the past couple of years, a self-appointed carer, a duty that he took very seriously and carried out with great humility and respect.

Garfield had fallen downstairs twice, and, after the second time, Timmy had taken it upon himself to lie across the top of the stairs to stop Garfield from attempting to get down by himself. Garfield would call out to me and I'd come and get him down, but Timmy wouldn't move from his position until I had Garfield safely in my arms.

I have a wonderful photograph taken the split second that Garfield tried to get past Timmy's protective barrier, and Timmy had thrust his left front paw out across Garfield to prevent him from going down the stairs. At the same time, he shouted at Garfield; a long sharp 'Naaoo' sound and Garfield stood back from the edge and waited for me.

Timmy always accompanied Garfield into the garden, either for just a breath of fresh air or for the more usual toilet breaks. While I'd be massaging his abdomen to help him pass urine, Timmy would wait discreetly a few feet away or he'd go into another part of the garden on the pretext of seeing how the sweet peas were faring.

Long before I realised it, Timmy began guiding Garfield to his food bowl, or the water dish, and other places that Garfield wanted to go. A visit to see Kevin confirmed what Timmy had known for some time: Garfield was losing his vision in his right eye.

Timmy would also call me if Garfield wet himself. Garfield had arthritis and couldn't lift his legs high enough to get into the litter tray, so he would do his toilet alongside the tray on the newspaper I put underneath it. At night, he lay on a little sofa in his bed in the dining room, with Timmy lying across the front of him to stop him falling out. Some of the other cats also lay on this little sofa to keep Garfield company and take over duties should Timmy wish to go out himself.

In the mornings, he'd still be lying next to Garfield and poor Garfield would look terribly embarrassed because he'd wet his bed. I never told him off for these little indiscretions as I knew he couldn't help it, but sometimes it would happen during the day and Timmy would call out to me at the top of his voice and I'd run to see what was wrong. Timmy would move aside almost as if he was pointing to the wet patch, and I'd stroke his head, thanking him. I'd lift Garfield up and carry him to the bathroom where I'd lay him on a towel and gently wash him. He would always kiss me afterwards as if to thank me and apologise for inconveniencing me.

Timmy had done so much for Garfield in the last two or three years of Garfield's life and I knew that losing him would be very hard for Timmy to accept.

A friend from church called round the next morning to take me to the vets with Garfield's body while I made arrangements to take him to the pet crematorium in Cambridge later in the week. I hated to leave him there but needed to as the weather was so hot it would not have been hygienic to keep him at home. As if they knew, each of the cats came in to see Garfield again and kissed him. Timmy sniffed him before he gave him a final wash. Meowing quietly, he kissed him for the last time before I took Garfield back up to the vets.

Later that day, Tuesday, my son Paul took me to the hospital where he was to meet the consultant, Dr W, and I had to have more blood tests. She explained to Paul what was going on with my blood and marrow and asked if he had any questions. Paul asked if he or David could be considered for stem cell donation, but as they were my sons, they would only be half a match for me – whereas there would be a one in four chance that my brothers would be an exact tissue match.

The results of the blood tests taken that day were surprising. My blood had stabilised! The levels had been going down since February and the date for admission into hospital to begin the chemotherapy was delayed by another week. I also mentioned about Garfield having to be put to sleep the previous evening and that I had to arrange his funeral. Dr W quite understood. I said the extra week at home would help with continuing to get the house organised ready for Steve to move in while I was in hospital.

Although Paul realised my situation was serious, he doesn't

like illness and when I asked him if he was all right, he just nodded. I asked if he wanted to discuss anything or ask me questions about what was going to happen, but he declined. Like many people, Paul adopts the attitude if unpleasant things are not discussed, they will go away, a bit like putting unpaid bills in a drawer out of sight hoping they'll get magically paid. If only life were that simple.

David came back from his holiday in Spain the following morning. I rang him and asked if he could come over as I had two lots of news to tell him, both of which were serious. Poor David – coming home from a great holiday buzzing with energy and the good feeling that comes from having a tan and relaxing for two weeks - and now I was about to prick his bubble with two lots of unpleasant news.

Before David's arrival, though, Geoff the vicar from my church came, and we discussed how best people from the church could be of help to my family and me. I'd made a coffee and walnut sponge cake the day before, only I'd forgotten to put the walnuts in. And because I had to use a foul-tasting mouthwash as part of the preventative treatment now, I couldn't taste food or drink properly – everything tasted funny to me. So, I didn't realise that the coffee butter cream filling was on the very strong side.

After Geoff went, the Will man came. A slightly built man with greying hair and a small beard, he was dressed smartly in a dark blue suit. Obviously writing a Will was serious enough to warrant the right attire for the occasion, and I was impressed.

I had never made a Will before and had no idea how to go about it. Suddenly having to deal with the fact that I could die made me feel very vulnerable and I just wanted to cry – but because the Will man was there, I held the tears back.

I told him about the leukaemia, and he was shocked. To him, and indeed anyone who saw me, I looked so well that it was hard to believe there was anything seriously wrong with me. He was very helpful and explained everything thoroughly to me, what the best way to do this was, and how to do that, and then he was on his way and I tried not to think about the Will being read out at some sombre gathering of relatives and friends in the near future.

And then David arrived, looking fit and tanned after his holiday. While I was making a drink for us in the kitchen, he sat in the lounge waiting for me. Only then did I realise that my 'get well' cards and 'sorry for your loss' cards were on display in the lounge, and David would put two and two together.

He called out from the lounge: 'is one of the pieces of bad news about Garfield?' With tears in my eyes I told him what happened. David had always loved animals and I had promised him that we would get a kitten or a cat when we moved into our home. Back in May 1986, a year after we moved into our house, David had come screeching into the house on his way home from school, and exclaimed excitedly: 'Mum, Mum, you must come and look at these kittens.'

So, we did. We went straight back to the local pet shop, a short walk from our house, to look at the two beautiful little ginger kittens. As we couldn't make up our minds which one to have, we brought both home, and Garfield and Biggles made our house a home.

Now here he was, almost thirty-four years of age being told that only two days earlier Garfield had been put to sleep and 'Oh, and by the way, your mother may be dying of leukaemia.'

He insisted on coming to the hospital with me the following Wednesday for my blood tests and to meet Dr W. In the meantime, he went on the Internet and began looking for websites to give us both some information.

On Friday of that week, another friend, Almeric, who had once been my boss when I worked at a local hospital as a secretary/PA, arrived at my house at 9.15 in the morning and we drove to the vets' surgery to collect Garfield. The journey to Cambridge normally took about an hour and three-quarters and we did it, without breaking any speed restrictions, in just over an hour, the traffic having been unusually slight that morning.

We were too early for our 11.30 slot, so we continued past the crematorium heading into Royston, which is in Hertfordshire. We parked and headed for the Corn Exchange which is a group of buildings set around a courtyard. It was quite easy to imagine how life would have been one hundred years earlier in such wonderful historic surroundings. In amongst the different types of small shops was a lovely café which sold home-baked cakes and pies and the usual range of drinks and refreshments.

Almeric had hot chocolate and crumpets, and I had a cappuccino and a scone. It was a very hot day, and despite the sadness of the occasion, there was an almost holiday type feeling about sitting outside, enjoying the sun and eating something slightly naughty.

We made our way back to the crematorium and I went to the reception area. I was told to bring Garfield and then they would talk us through what would happen. Having brought four of my other cats here in the past, including Biggles, Garfield's brother, when he was eleven, I knew the ropes, but each time I'd been back, the way things were done had altered very slightly.

We were taken into a room where there was a metal tray into which I placed Garfield in his box. He was lying on soft towels and had a nice blanket folded up as a pillow. His night-time teddies, BananaMan and Moo, were tucked up under his front paw just as they used to be when he went to sleep at night – and now, together, they were going with him on this final journey. I had a few moments alone with him, when I told him again how much I loved him, how much I would always love him, and how much I would miss him. I thanked him for all the times he lay beside me when I was recovering from various illnesses or following stays in hospitals after operations, and I thanked him for all the times he made me laugh – which was often. I told him that he was the best cat in the world and that I would never, ever, forget him.

And then it was time for our last goodbye. He went through a red velvet curtain and I saw him no more. As it would take about an hour and a half to two hours for Garfield's ashes to be ready, Almeric and I were given directions to a nearby garden centre. It had a nice restaurant attached, which came highly recommended, and so, to pass the time, we wandered around the garden centre. Afterwards, although I had little appetite, we had a bit of lunch, but my heart wasn't in looking at plants and shrubs.

We came back a bit later and Garfield's ashes were waiting for me in a nice little box with an artificial flower on the top. I brought him home and placed the box in the top of the wardrobe alongside the boxes of my other cats that had passed away over the years in my bedroom wardrobe. Sadly, I had quite a collection now.

Chapter 3 – Reality sets in

Dr W, my consultant, was seeing me on a weekly basis and each week the blood tests were quite surprising. My blood count had been falling to worrying levels since the initial blood tests back in February and now, in June, it had suddenly stabilised which meant that the date for admission to begin chemotherapy was put further and further back. On the third or fourth week of this trend, when Dr W told me the news, I punched the air and I said, 'Praise the Lord!'

She gave me a strange look. 'Did I say that out loud?' I asked, smiling awkwardly.

'Yes,' she nodded back at me.

Feeling a tad embarrassed I told her that I was a Christian and people all over the world were praying for me and that I believed in God, the power of prayer and the fact that He can heal me and I believed that I would be healed. I so didn't want to go into hospital to have chemotherapy and I was praying fervently that I would be healed BEFORE that happened.

To my surprise, she said: 'I'm a Christian as well, and I believe in the power of prayer and that God can heal you. But I have to be seen to be doing my job in getting you the best treatment available for your situation.'

We smiled at each other. We were on the same page! What a great comfort it was to know that my very own consultant also believed in God – now I felt I could talk freely about my feelings, hopes and aspirations without fear of being thought of as an idiot.

Dr W gave me an A4 booklet-type newsletter one day from the Leukaemia Care Research people. I took it home, devoured every page of information, and then I rang the free number to subscribe. There were many helpful booklets dealing with a very wide range of topics within the world of leukaemia. I didn't know, for example, that there were more than 700 different types of leukaemia, but some were much more serious than others.

Within a few days, a wonderful package arrived from Leukaemia Care Research with a couple of back copies of the newsletter and a whole raft of information. I read one of the newsletters from cover to cover. It contained two stories written by people who had experienced the same leukaemia (AML) that I had. Both had had terrible setbacks; both had been in intensive care a couple of times in their respective hospitals and both had come near to death, and it seemed they were far from being 'safe' now.

Suddenly, the enormity of what I had wrong with me hit me full in the face. I crumbled like a tree being blown over in the gales and I started to cry. At first, I just howled out loud like some demented banshee. I hadn't had the support I'd hoped for from certain quarters in my family and, as a result, I felt so terribly alone and utterly terrified with this 'big' thing inside me, which was going to cause horrendous problems, if the two stories I'd just read were anything to go by. I didn't want to die. I had my sons, grandchildren, cats, friends, website and many other interests that I didn't want to leave behind or let go. I cried because I suddenly felt tiny, insignificant and unloved.

I cried, too, for Garfield. Since having him put to sleep, I hadn't grieved. I'd been too preoccupied in dealing with all those lists, getting the house tidied up for when Steve came, and other minutiae that kept me from dwelling on my loss.

It broke my heart to lose Garfield – ours was the longest relationship I'd ever had – and I missed his calming presence. He always knew when I was ill, upset, worried or just down in the dumps. He'd put a paw on my leg or my face and lick me – and all would be right with the world again. I'd had such a special relationship with Garfield, that although I had five other cats, none of them were as in sync with me as he'd been.

After a couple of hours, the wailing simmered down to hiccoughing sobs as I racked my brains trying to think of someone I could ring up to just listen to my fears. A strange thing happened when I first started to tell people about having leukaemia. Almost immediately, they would interrupt my story to tell me about a family member or friend who had also had leukaemia and who'd died within seconds of diagnosis. This was obviously not the kind of thing I wanted to hear about – not that I was unsympathetic to their news, but wasn't there anyone who had survived?

But why do people do that? Why do they tell you dreadful things when you are going through a life-changing situation? I remembered back to when I was expecting my first son, Paul, and just before I went into labour I heard all these 'horror' stories from women who thought it was vital that they tell me just how much they had 'suffered' during labour. What purpose does it serve other than to put the fear of God into you?

The other thing was the unpredictability in the way people responded. Most people were in shock as I was, especially as I still looked robustly healthy, but one person just put the phone down on me right after I told her the results of the bone marrow test, not wanting to talk about it anymore. The same person would often deliberately start an argument with me when I tried to update her about how the weekly blood tests were progressing, and it felt as though me having leukaemia was incredibly inconvenient for her to deal with; it became all about her and how she felt – not about me and what I was feeling.

I was very upset, confused and very angry. Living alone with just my cats for company, I needed to have someone I could talk to. Someone who would just let me get all my fears out without constant interruptions or a stream of platitudes which meant absolutely nothing if you analysed them – they just made the person who said them feel better but they certainly didn't make me feel better.

All I wanted was to have an arm put round my shoulder; a kind word of support, of love, even – if necessary – a white lie – that all would be well. I needed someone that would let me rant, rave, scream and shout if I wanted to, and for them not to mind. But it felt like I was in some kind of solitary confinement where I was not allowed to be myself or discuss what was happening to me because it was too difficult for others to hear – never mind what it was like for me.

A few television programmes had had leukaemia as a storyline but the person who'd been diagnosed with it didn't survive. And a film on Hallmark followed the same route, so I was left reeling with the knowledge that I was possibly going to die, and I couldn't discuss my feelings with anyone. The threat of having the phone put down on me, or an argument ensuing, was too distressing for me. The fact that I remained cheerful whenever I met any of my friends or spoke to people over the phone, was because I knew, without a shadow of doubt, that if I acted the way I felt – terribly frightened – they wouldn't be in a position to help me because they were reacting in a negative way which was not the solution I needed. They were relying on me to keep strong for them! It was ok for them to break down and cry and need me to hold them up, but it wasn't ok for me to show my true fears and feelings.

Most of my family members and friends saw me as someone who was strong. I had coped with some dreadful situations in my life, usually without help, and had always remained upbeat and positive. I had been someone that people often turned to in times of need because I could usually offer practical help and advice.

The thing with cancer is that it strips away a person's dignity so that, generally, they are reliant on others. I believe that those closest to me couldn't deal with the idea that my once bubbly persona could become ravaged by the disease and that, somehow, I'd be 'different'. Their own fears, as real as they may have been at the time, kept them from reaching out to me. This meant that I was about to face the worst challenge of my entire life almost completely by myself. Another friend, Dale, pointed out to me at the time, 'when you're going through the mill, you certainly find out who your friends are.'

And I think seeing me in a more helpless situation frightened people because to some, I was their rock. Rocks are strong; rocks don't get life-threatening illnesses and rocks don't let you down.

Generally, as a Christian, I try to be polite to everyone and it wouldn't have entered my head at the time to have challenged the people who told me that a family member had died of leukaemia, but I think now I would actually say to them: 'And this news helps me how?' And as for the person who put the phone down on me: when I rang back a few days later and asked how she was, she snapped at me: 'How do you think I am?' I think that now I would be tempted to snap back at her: 'And how do you think *I'M* feeling? This isn't exactly a picnic for me either, you know.'

All that served to do was to make me feel very isolated and lonely – and scared. And it seemed that there wasn't anyone I could talk to about my feelings because people would interrupt constantly and tell me other things to 'take my mind off it'. I didn't want my mind taken off it. I needed to talk about things, to rationalise everything and put it in neat compartments where I could deal with it as, and when, I wanted to. I needed to be allowed to make sense of what was going on. I think, on reflection, people didn't want to have to think about my situation, so they wouldn't have to deal with it. That's why they changed the subject, so they were let off the hook.

I prayed. Constantly. God was the one true immovable force that didn't let me down. While I spilled out all my fears and worries to him, I wished there was someone I could share my thoughts with, who could take some of the burden from me.

Finally, I thought of my cousin Colin, so I rang him up, sobbing an almost incoherent message on his answer phone because he was out at the time. Almost immediately, though, he rang back and bless his heart, he fulfilled the criteria. I cried and blubbed and probably didn't make any sense at all. He listened without saying a word, speaking only occasionally when I took time to draw breath and wipe my nose. Then, he asked me if I was ok and did I want to make a drink to help calm me down.

He was absolutely great and just the right person I needed – the only pity being that he lives in Australia and I'm in the UK!

Fortunately for me, Colin also has a faith system and, over the months that followed, we would often talk about how we could see God's hand in everything. It was good to be able to feel so relaxed talking to him about all my innermost fears, something I just couldn't discuss with anyone in my immediate family or within my close circle of friends.

At the end of our marathon two-hour conversation, which was on Colin's phone bill, I felt so much better and I realised I had finally stopped crying. I wasn't even sobbing anymore, and I felt as if a huge weight had been lifted off my shoulders.

Another Christian friend of mine, Catherine, once said to me that 'haloes are painted on by artists' and that comment has always stuck in my mind. I realise that all of us fall very short when dealing with bad news and although I'd like to think that I would be helpful to the person in need, there is a possibility that I, too, wouldn't react the way they would want me to when telling me their bad news. School doesn't teach you the lessons you need for dealing with life and all that it throws at you.

The trouble was that for me, I was in the position of having to buoy everyone else up. No one was lifting me up and supporting me – I had to do that for myself, in addition, I had to support those who weren't coping with my news as well. It was a tough time and I believe that some people actually didn't take me seriously when I told them I had leukaemia. Because at that point I hadn't collapsed in a heap or curled up in the foetal position and declared that 'life wasn't fair', my general positive attitude bewildered them. How could I possibly have a life-threatening illness and still be a bubbly, happy person when all around me were in disbelief?

It was even suggested by someone quite close to me that if I was healed before I had chemotherapy, they wouldn't believe that I'd ever had leukaemia! Incredulous, I asked if they knew what chemotherapy did to someone and the reply was 'I know they go bald.'

Then I explained in graphic detail exactly what chemotherapy does to the body. Yes, it does what it says on the tin and zaps the spot, so to speak, but it can cause cancer in other parts of the body some years later. Did they really want me to go through all that just to prove to them I had leukaemia? Apparently, their lack of faith meant they could not believe that prayer could make me better, if I recovered it meant that I had not had leukaemia in the first place.

The problem was I didn't look ill and didn't have a grey drawn look about my face, and my eternal optimism and faith possibly belied the fact that I was, in fact, quite seriously ill.

But, having spoken to Colin, and read those accounts in the Leukaemia Care magazine, all of a sudden, I realised that I was no longer in that place called 'Denial'. Suddenly I was in the 'Real World' and now I had to get on and deal with things.

The phrase: 'Rearranging the chairs on the Titanic' is a byword for utter pointlessness, but in practice it often happens; someone trying to take their mind off a real problem, will fuss over an absurd detail.

This is exactly what I had been doing without realising it. In my sense of denial, I flapped around being terribly busy, but achieving absolutely nothing. Now I had to face the music, accept what was happening to me, and going to happen to me, and prepare for the fight of my life.

Chapter 4 – Life gets more scary

On 2 August I woke up with a slight sore throat. I sneezed my way downstairs and wondered if this was going to be a full-on cold or whether it was just a minor adaptation to the change in the weather. July had been the hottest on record since records began in 1756 or something. Then suddenly, at the beginning of August, the weather had drastically changed.

Rain was desperately needed in the south eastern corner of England where I lived, and a hose pipe ban had been in force for a couple of months. But the temperature had plummeted, and it felt really cold. Having spent most of the days throughout July in shorts and tee shirts, and the nights lying on top of the bed without any covers or clothes, I now felt very cold indeed.

It was not surprising that the symptoms of a cold were manifesting – but I was scared. Getting a cold meant that I might have to go into hospital which I didn't want to do as the house still wasn't straight. The back bedroom, which I used as an office, was still in a terrible mess and certainly not fit for Steve to use as his bedroom. I didn't know how long I might have to stay in hospital if I did have to go in at such short notice. Would Steve even be able to come at the drop of a hat? There were too many things to be concerned about and I didn't want to have to worry about anything.

So, I did what I always do. I prayed. As it was a Wednesday, I went to the early morning communion service at my church,

St. Paul's. I always enjoyed the peace of those brief services and the fact that because there are only fifteen or twenty of us there, it is more informal. But towards the end of the service, I began to feel quite unwell, so rather than staying to chat to people afterwards, I hurried home.

I thought that having a sleep might help me feel better, so making myself comfortable on the sofa with two of my cats, Billy and Sam, nearby, I slept for almost an hour. My throat felt worse. I made a drink and looked for the hospital's telephone number.

I was put through to the chemotherapy nurse, Cathy, whom I'd met on the first morning of my diagnosis. I could hear her tap-tapping and realised she was searching for my records on the computer. She said that I might have to go in for a blood test. It was almost 11.45am and I didn't feel like going. I told her that I had some antibiotics handy and asked if it would be ok to take them? She said that she'd bleep one of the consultants in the absence of mine who was on holiday, and she'd ring me straight back. Within a few minutes she rang back to say that I could take the antibiotics but if my sore throat worsened, if my temperature went up, or if I got a fever, I was to ring up the chemotherapy nurses and they would tell me what to do.

Relieved, I then went back to the church, with a coffee and walnut cake I had made the day before, having remembered to put the walnuts in this time. On the first Wednesday of each month, we have a 'bring and share' lunch at church and each person brings something to share for lunch. I dropped the cake off, getting a friend to cut it into slices, and I went into the church for some quiet time.

I sat there, alone in the church. I looked up at the high

vaulted ceiling and took in the beams, and then my eyes looked around at the beautiful stained-glass windows. I felt I was in God's presence and I began to pray. Within a few minutes I was overcome with tears and couldn't stop crying. My entire body was shaking with tears and grief, fear and worry. How long I sat there crying, I don't know. But all of a sudden, I was aware of an arm being put around my shoulders and my friend Brenda, praying for me.

Feeling vulnerable again and scared that this cold could cause me to die, I shared my fears with her. I know I rambled on about the lack of support from certain family members, the back bedroom being in a mess, and everything that needed to be done, so that I could go into hospital without worrying, had just piled up. Having CFS meant that I rarely had sufficient energy to do the simplest of tasks at times. Coupled with the intense heat of July, I had been unable to do very much in the way of decluttering to get the house ready for Steve to stay.

Each week my blood tests had stabilised and the date for going into hospital to begin treatment kept being deferred for another few weeks. After the initial frantic list-making exercises, life had settled into a more rhythmic pace. Although in the beginning, I had contacted everyone I could think of, I found it very hard going to tidy through the piles of papers on my desk or put books and other things away in their proper places.

Some days, I would be sofa-bound for much of the day, exhausted, unable to even read or knit. I was acutely aware that there was still a lot of clutter to clear and plenty of dusting – and probably the removal of fossilised spiders or mummified mice left over from Ollie's nocturnal adventures – so mentally, I prepared a 'schedule of works' that I could realistically work through and accomplish.

I have faced and coped with many huge hurdles in my life, but this was very much a different thing all together. I had nothing in my armoury with which to fight, although my faith was holding up, I still felt that I might not come through this.

Prayer is a marvellous thing. I often think of people who profess to not having a belief system and wonder who they call on in times of worry. My Mother doesn't believe in God, but she blames Him for all the troubles in the world. I once said to her that as she doesn't believe in Him, she couldn't really blame Him when things went wrong, because that would be saying that He did exist after all. She got cross with me and changed the subject. But she's not alone in her assumptions and as much as I love my Mother, I know that God is there because I have the sure-fire feeling of His presence with me.

So, for me, prayer is an important and integral part of my day. Chatting to God about this and that is a bit like me having a phone conversation with one of my best friends. But I also commit time to praying for other people and other more serious situations. And, many times I've seen answer to prayer, so I had every confidence in God that this new experience I was going through, not only would He be with me every step of the way, but that because half the world was praying for me, He would actually heal me.

I say half the world was praying for me because many of the subscribers to the monthly Mewsletter, had contacted me and asked if I minded being put on their prayer lists, or prayer chains. As this involved hundreds of people throughout the world, it was, therefore, reasonable and entirely feasible that half the world *could* be praying for me. I also had affiliations with many of the local churches within my area, and others nearby, all of which had active weekly prayers groups. As I was well known, my health situation was prayed for on a weekly basis by many, if not all, of these churches.

Brenda held me tight and prayed for me. I don't remember what she said but I do remember a feeling of utter peace surrounding me and engulfing me. We talked about how people could help me – that all I had to do was to ask.

Asking for help was something that didn't come easily to me. In the past, I'd asked family members or friends for help, or I'd expected help at times of difficulty, and it hadn't been forthcoming. So, I'd developed a tough resilient outer shell and just got on with things myself. It had been said to me once, by someone within my family, that I was so independent and capable that I didn't need any help. I was only independent and capable because whenever I had asked for help, it was never available. The most traumatic experiences in my life I'd been through, I'd handled myself, without any help from my family.

Brenda and I went back into the coffee lounge where others had gathered, and I had a piece of the coffee and walnut sponge cake. Despite still having to use the horrid mouthwash, I noticed that it did taste a lot better than the one I'd made previously where the coffee filling had been a bit strong. Geoff, our vicar, had eaten it anyway, and told me it was lovely, bless him.

Clothed in a mantle of prayer, I felt able to continue this 'mystery' journey along its unknown route and, somehow, I felt I was going to be all right.

Chapter 5 – Fantastic news!

My brother Tony is a tissue match! On Friday 11 August he rang me from work and asked if I had a minute. I replied that I did. He asked me if I was sitting down. I replied that I was. And then he told me that he'd heard back from the transplant co-ordinator at King's College Hospital that he's a full tissue match for either bone marrow or stem cell transplant.

Tears sprang to my eyes as I sat there. I didn't know what to say other than 'thank you!' The next part of the journey was beginning!

In early July, Tony had been sent all the necessary phials and syringes needed to take to his own doctor's surgery. They were to carry out the blood tests which he then had to forward back to King's College Hospital.

As the stuff arrived a day or so before he was going to Tenerife on a two-week holiday with his wife Jackie, and their two sons, Lee and Martyn, I suggested that he wait until he came back from his holiday before completing the blood tests. He already had a lot to do and trying to fix a doctor's appointment at very short notice wasn't fair to him. A few weeks of waiting wouldn't hurt, and I knew that the search had already begun on the donors' list to try to find a tissue match.

Our youngest brother, Garry, did not take part in the blood test to see if he was a tissue match because of health issues. Even if he had taken the tests, there wouldn't have been any problems with him passing anything on to me as his blood would have been screened for dozens and dozens of illnesses.

I know when Tony did go to King's to meet the transplant co-ordinator, Elizabeth Tatum, in the Apheresis department, he had to have various health tests done, which included an ECG and he had to undergo a barrage of other blood tests looking for any and all kinds of infections, illnesses, diseases and such like. No stone was left unturned to ensure that Tony's stem cells would be pure as the driven snow when they finally made their transition to my own body.

Poor Tony, having dozens of blood tests at one time, reminded me of the time when the most memorable and impressive number of phials of blood I had taken in any one session was an awesome seventeen. An incredible amount and at the time, I remarked to the nurse that my arm felt limp as I was certain it was completely drained of any blood. This reminded me of the Tony Hancock sketch 'The Blood Donor'. Seeing a phial of blood taken he exclaimed: 'Well, that's very nearly an armful!' She laughed when I mentioned it and said that I would be surprised at how little blood was actually removed.

So now that we knew Tony was a tissue match, the search on the donors' register could relax – as could I and the medical teams involved. We knew that in time, once I'd had treatment – chemotherapy – Tony's stem cells would be harvested, and they would be transplanted into me.

I was still hopeful, however, that with all the constant prayers being said for me not only in the local churches I was associated with, but also throughout the world, that the need for chemotherapy would be redundant and that Tony wouldn't need to give up his stem cells for me.

To say we were both excited would be an understatement.

But we both experienced our own individual fears, which oddly, we didn't voice to each other. Tony also has Chronic Fatigue Syndrome and although the transplant co-ordinators at King's College Hospital knew this and said it wouldn't matter, I did wonder if it would make a difference to how Tony felt in himself. My train journeys to and from King's College Hospital were only half an hour each way and I could do each journey, door to door, in more or less an hour. But for Tony, it was a three-train journey there and back again – six trains in all taking up to two – three hours each way, so he was going to be far more tired than I was.

I didn't want him to 'suffer' or experience any relapses with his Chronic Fatigue Syndrome, and I even questioned a consultant at King's College Hospital at one point on the validity and sense in allowing Tony to donate his stem cells. I didn't want him to become more unwell because of me. I told the consultant that I would rather wait for a tissue match from the donor register rather than put Tony through additional stress, which may later cause him to have a relapse. Incredibly, I was told that the initial search hadn't produced any matches. Shocked, I asked the consultant what would happen if there weren't any matches. I was told that they would just make me as comfortable as they could, and basically wait for me to die.

So, Tony was the only chance I had.

Chapter 6 – Things are beginning to happen

Thursday 9 November 2006, I had to go into hospital to have a Hickman Line inserted. After months of to-ing and fro-ing from Queen Mary's Hospital, Sidcup, Kent, and King's College Hospital, in Denmark Hill, London, I was about to begin treatment within the next few days. Professor Mufti, at King's, had explained to me that if I wanted to be home in time for Christmas, then the first month's course of chemotherapy would have to start in early November. That meant a trip to Queen Mary's to have a Hickman Line put in. A Hickman Line has three 'udder' type attachments or lumens, through which chemotherapy and any other drugs or treatment can be fed. It was also possible to draw blood from it to save frequent vein pricking. I had good veins in the crook of each arm but for some people, the constant use of the same veins can cause them to collapse making it painful and impossible to draw any blood.

The day didn't go as I hoped! I reported to the ward just after 9.00am as instructed having had nothing to eat since 7.00pm the previous evening. I was not best pleased to hear that my 'slot' was at 2.30pm. I was told this at 9.30am and my heart sank. My friend, Almeric, who had taken me to the hospital, intended to wait with me so that we could go to lunch afterward. Now it would be around 5.00pm before I might be able to go home.

I was in a room by myself, so I just lay on the bed and dozed or read my book, trying not to think about food. I felt anxious and nervous yet optimistic the prayers that my church friends, and the subscribers to my website were saying for me, might be answered and that, at the eleventh hour, I wouldn't have to go through with the chemotherapy.

Anna, the SHO, had rung me two days earlier and told me to bring an overnight bag just in case I had to stay in – but quickly put my fears at rest by saying it wasn't likely to happen.

But my 2.30pm slot came and went. A two-month old baby had come in as an emergency. Eventually, the anaesthetist, Dr Chris Palin, came to explain the procedure. As I am a total 'Wuss' when it comes to pain, I wanted to know if it would hurt much. He reassured me that whilst it was uncomfortable it wouldn't be that painful.

I would be awake, given a local anaesthetic and sedation to help me relax. It wouldn't put me to sleep but would sufficiently relax me that I wouldn't really notice what was happening.

Wheeled into theatre about 4.30, our first problem was due to my 'over insulation' at my collar bone level. The big juicy vein which is the one favoured for the Hickman Line couldn't be located on the scan. Apparently, I had a fantastic vein in my neck, and this was used with my permission instead. A radio playing hit songs in the background caused much bantering and giggling. Dr Palin singing along to Chaka Khan's 'I'm every woman' prompted one of the junior doctors in attendance to suggest that Chris probably shouldn't sing along to that type of song. I felt completely at ease with my surroundings and what was happening to me.

Every now and then, I yelped when something involving a smidge of pain occurred, so I was given another dollop of sedation.

I was finally returned to my ward with Chris advising that as I live alone, I should stay the night so that I could be monitored. Not the words I wanted to hear but under the circumstances, the best course of action for me.

A cheese and tomato sandwich was found for me and I fell upon it hungrily. There had to be something else, surely – I hadn't eaten for almost twenty-four hours and felt quite faint. Another nurse scavenged two soft rolls and two pats of butter (no knife) from somewhere, so I managed to spread the butter somehow using its foil wrap.

After I'd eaten the rolls I remembered, too late, that wheat-based products caused me to bloat up but, at that moment in time, I couldn't care less. I prayed that God would spare me from any unpleasant side effects and tried to settle down to sleep.

A wonderful nurse called Marva came in to flush the line as it had already been used for a bag of antibiotics to flow into me. The wound under the dressing had been bleeding and she cleaned it all up for me before replacing the dressing. We talked about Faith and the power of prayer and how God heals today. I was greatly uplifted by talking to her, and I thanked the Lord for bringing her to me when I needed it.

Surprisingly, since I'd had two cups of coffee on returning to the ward, I managed to sleep quite well. Usually, I drink decaffeinated coffee as 'proper' coffee keeps me awake for hours. The Hickman position on the right side of my neck meant I could lay comfortably on my left side, which was my preferred sleeping position.

I woke a few times in the night to use the bathroom but I was so tired that I managed to go straight back to sleep after.

At 6.15am a nurse came in to take my blood pressure, temperature etc. I told her it was my favourite time of day to be woken up, but I don't think she realised that I was, in fact, joking.

The next interruption came at 7.00am when I was given a cup of coffee. It wasn't decaffeinated coffee but, as I was quite thirsty, so I accepted it gratefully.

By now my stomach had woken up and was complaining loudly. I knew that breakfast didn't come much before 8.30 am, so I tried some diversionary tactics.

I tried to sleep, and for a while it worked, but I soon became aware of the great cavernous feeling in my stomach.

So, I decided to pray. 'Lord,' I asked, 'please take away this empty feeling and fill me with the fruits of the Spirit. Fill me with love to share with all I meet today; fill me with joy that I might smile in all circumstances and fill me with peace that the worries and doubts I have about the coming weeks of chemotherapy will be like dust particles – to be swept away.'

Having prayed this prayer, I realised that I no longer felt that gnawing ache of hunger. God had, indeed, filled me with the fruits of the Spirit!

When breakfast finally came, I plumped for a bowl of porridge, some orange juice, banana and another coffee. It was like a banquet and I gave thanks for such a welcome repast.

I had to stay in hospital for most of the day so that I could be monitored and finally, around 5.00pm, my friend Gary came to collect me, and I went home to my poor, bewildered cats.

The following morning, Steve came round, and I discussed with him all the necessary things he'd need to know for the coming weeks while I was in hospital. Having lost Garfield back in June, five cats remained - Billy, Timmy, Sam, Ricky and Ollie - and they were familiar with him as he'd looked after them before when I'd been on holiday. Going into hospital, though, for an indefinite stay was not exactly a holiday and I knew Steve was quite nervous at having the uncertain responsibility of feline care.

I was fervently hoping, that when I reached the hospital on Monday morning to begin my first course of chemotherapy, the doctors would suddenly burst into the room and say that they've found the 'real' Pauline Dewberry and I could go home – panic over. I still felt well, and I looked robustly healthy, so it was very hard for me to accept that I had anything wrong with me, let alone leukaemia.

On the Sunday, in the afternoon, my son Paul took me to Queen Mary's so that I could have an injection in my stomach. This stimulates the white blood cells to be where they're needed for chemotherapy. It only took a few moments, but I was quite anxious.

I didn't want to have chemotherapy – I had heard too much about the side effects to know that it wasn't for me, but there was nothing else that could be done. In order for my body to be rid of the leukaemic cells and to prepare for receiving the stem cells donated by my brother, Tony, the only course of action available to me was chemotherapy.

A couple of days before I went into hospital to have the Hickman Line put in, I'd done my Christmas shopping with my neighbour. Not knowing how long I was going to be in hospital having chemotherapy, and how I would feel when I came out of hospital after the first course, I thought it prudent to get as much done towards Christmas as possible. I would be neutropenic and unable to mix with people or go into crowded places for fear of catching colds, flu and other infections. So, I spent the next few days wrapping up presents and distributing them to Paul and his son, Matthew, and David, Tanya, Lee and Demi and other friends.

I was all set now. I just had to wait until Monday and the start of chemotherapy. Come on God, it's up to You, now!

Chapter 7 – The chemotherapy journey begins – almost!

I often have a recurring dream where I'm riding a bike and I just cycle through all the places I've lived throughout my life. I usually start off through the streets of Edgware, Middlesex where I grew up. We lived on a council estate, which backed onto fields, and there was a railway line which used to go through Mill Hill East and beyond. Scratch Woods – before it became the service station – was our playground and, with my two younger brothers, Ken and Tony and various other neighbourhood children, we'd make our camps and tree houses among the rhododendron bushes and oak trees, our imaginations running riot as we innocently played.

Then I find myself cycling through country lanes or along wide roads. I have no idea where I am or where I am going and, although there is something vaguely familiar about the scenery around me, I don't really know it. I don't feel frightened by where I am or where I'm heading. The sun is always shining and there is a general sense of wellbeing, so I'm not unhappy about doing all this cycling. It's strange because I'm not someone who is a health freak and the only exercise I get usually is to bend over to pick up one of my cats, stroke them, and put them back down again or picking up their food and water bowls a couple of times a day – that's as far as it goes.

I dreamt this dream a lot prior to going into hospital to begin my course of chemotherapy. I didn't know if there was a 'message' in the dream, or if I was meant to feel that the 'journey' would be a breeze. I can often interpret other people's dreams but not always my own. But when the day came for me to go into hospital, I didn't feel nervous or worried.

As a child I used to spend a lot of time on my own in my bedroom. I would often be sent there for some misdemeanour or other – half the time I don't know what I'd done wrong, if indeed, I'd done anything wrong. I think it was just to get me out of the way. But those times spent on my own were not wasted - I'd retreat into my books. I was an early and avid reader, and I wondered if I would ever be able to write a book which might hold someone spellbound, sitting on the toilet in the bathroom, while trying to get out of doing the washing up, which is what I used to do.

And somehow, I always felt invincible – the books came to life while I read them, and the heroes or heroines always taught me lessons on how to become a 'better' person. I longed to be good like Heidi and perhaps be more loved than I felt I was.

I lost myself in all the children's classics; I immersed myself in each story, becoming the hero or heroine, taking on their characteristics or personalities. At least I thought I did. I think me trying to emulate Heidi, for example, largely went unnoticed.

With this ability to retreat into myself when times were tough, I think perhaps that was what I did when I began chemotherapy. I'd heard so many awful stories about what happens during chemotherapy, that part of me was probably very frightened indeed. Although my church friends were praying for me, I still went through most of this by myself without anyone with me to offer comfort or solace.

A friend of mine told me how she vomited constantly during

her treatment, and despite being given anti-emetics, she was still sick. If there is one thing I hate it's the physical act of throwing up and although I knew I would lose my hair, I was more concerned about this threat.

So, I put on a brave front, smiling as if I didn't have a care in the world. Of course, my faith in God was what held me together. I had no doubt, up till this point, that I hadn't achieved all I was meant to, and that God had much better things in store for me. I still fully believed He was going to heal me and that once the chemotherapy began, they would do some tests and find that the leukaemia had somehow miraculously disappeared, and I could go back home again – to continue my life, but on a greater level than I did before.

I also knew that sometimes death is seen as the ultimate healing - but I was hoping that I would be spared from this extreme form of healing. With people all over the world praying for me, how could I not recover and be a witness to God's great love and goodness?

So, when Monday 13 November came round, I think I was relieved that finally, something was going to happen. My blood count had started to dip. I became more anaemic which showed that the illness was progressing, and I was becoming sicker. Treatment was now a necessity and not something that would happen at a blurry future date.

I got up at 6.00am in order to pack all the things that I needed for a month's stay in hospital. Steve had arrived on Sunday morning, just as I was setting off for church, so I left him to get organised and settled.

Bob, my friend from the church group that I sang with, arrived about 9.00am to take me to the hospital. Poor Bob. I think he was slightly in awe of the amount of stuff I'd lined up in the hallway to take with me.

Originally, I had been told that I would be having six months of aggressive, intensive chemotherapy. So that I wouldn't go stir crazy, I had also been told that I might be allowed home for a weekend after each month's treatment. I wasn't really sure what I should take with me to keep myself occupied. I didn't know whether I would feel too sick to do anything or would be bored so I took a few books; some to read and some to review for my website, a notebook to jot down ideas for future stories and articles, and to keep a diary of events whilst in hospital. I took a manuscript that I was editing for a friend, knitting, a couple of CDs, one of which was a worship CD and the other was a cat's purr CD. I also took food in case I didn't like the hospital offerings, although I didn't know that there would be a time when I'd be neutropenic and therefore unable to eat most things. And I took a few boxes of my favourite decaffeinated cappuccino sachets as well as fruit juices.

All of this paraphernalia was arranged in two suitcases, a flight bag and three ASDA carrier bags. Smiling nervously, Bob loaded up his car.

The poor cats hadn't a clue what was going on and I felt bad that they had to face changes to their routine that I could do nothing about. Before Bob arrived, I cuddled and stroked each cat in turn, and told each one that he was a good boy and that Mummy loved him. I then said that Mummy was going into hospital for a little while and that when I came home, I might look a little bit different. I told them that Steve would look after them all and they were to be good boys for Steve, to take care of him in my absence, and not bring him any mice or birds as presents.

It felt a little bit like I was going on holiday in one sense, but I had never left them for a month before, and I wondered if they had any concept of time. Would they know when two weeks had passed by, for example, and be expecting me to come home? What would their reactions be when I came home with no hair, no eyebrows or eyelashes? Would they freak out? Would they back away from me and treat me with suspicion?

When I first started wearing glasses for reading and close work like sewing or knitting, Garfield used to get on my lap and reach up with his front paws to pull them off my face. He was possibly thinking I should have gone to Spec Savers. It took a long time for him to accept that I needed to wear glasses, and, at every opportunity, he would try to dislodge them. But as he had reacted to me having something different about me, I could only wonder how the cats might respond to my very changed appearance.

Would the hospital smell on my body upset them like it does when one of them has been to the vets'? The rest all gather round and sniff that one suspiciously before lashing out, believing him to be an intruder. I would no doubt find out when the month had passed.

Once again, I kissed my five cats, Billy, Timmy, Sam, Ricky and Ollie goodbye and told them that Mummy loved them and would see them soon. Then, with a heavy heart at leaving them for so long, and the fear of the unknown lurking in my mind, I followed Bob to his car to begin this next part of the journey.

Bob carried my bags to the room which was to be my home for the next four or five weeks. Before he left, he straightened the two lopsided pictures that had irritated me the previous week when I'd had the Hickman Line put in. And he put the clock right. A few weeks earlier the clocks had gone back an hour, so this was more than an hour fast. Then he hugged me and prayed for me before leaving. It was 9.50am.

Slowly I unpacked the case containing my clothes and put them away. Not knowing how long I was to actually stay in hospital, I didn't know what to pack. I had asked Keith, one of the chemotherapy nurses, what I should wear, and he said, 'Just wear something which is comfortable, not too tight and, as the nurses will need access to the Hickman Line, wear loose fitting tops.'

The hospital day is a long one, beginning usually around 5.00am and finishing whenever sleep finally overtakes one, so I felt it was very important to have a division between night and day. To that end, I packed a few nightdresses to change into before retiring each night, and some lightweight cotton 'bottoms' with some biggish baggy tee-shirts which co-ordinated with them to wear during the day.

It's easy to think of oneself as a 'sick' person when undergoing any form of long term treatment and, psychologically, I felt that to go through the motion of actually changing my clothes from nightwear to daywear, that it would somehow lift me from that status and I could just see myself as a part-time patient. I could still pretend to myself that I was in my cabin on a wonderful cruise somewhere; the only difference was that I wouldn't be sitting at the captain's table wearing a diaphanous gown and sparkling jewellery, laughing at his witty comments.

Next, I looked in the case containing my 'projects', books, DVDs, CDs, etc. As there were no storage facilities to put these things, I left them in the case and got a book out to read, plus my Bible, and study books for the time being. Then I tackled the three carrier bags; each containing oat-based snacks, or my favourite Cup-a-Soup; decaffeinated cappuccino sachets etc. It looked a phenomenal amount of stuff, but I was working to the principle that if I didn't like anything on the menu, I wouldn't starve at least.

While I was getting settled in, the cleaner came in the room and began pottering about in the bathroom. He asked me my name and told me his name was Alex. Then, much to my surprise, he asked me what I was doing later that day because he'd like to take me out for a meal. Laughing, I told him, that I would be in hospital for the rest of the day, for the foreseeable future, in fact.

He asked me how old I was, and I told him to guess. 'Thirty-six' was his reply. I told him that I would be fifty-six in August and he fell against the wall in shock. 'Fifty-six! You are fifty-six? But you only look about thirty-six!' he spluttered.

I thanked him for his very generous compliment and told him to visit me when my hair had fallen out, and then see how old I looked, and if he still wanted to take me out for a meal.

I'd only been in hospital just over an hour and already I'd been propositioned. I was so out of touch with flirting, receiving compliments and dating I didn't know what to say or do.

The day wore on and no one came to discuss what would be happening, or when it would happen. About 4.30 in the afternoon a doctor came, and he told me that they had decided to change an element of the chemotherapy and it would now start the following morning.

I felt deflated and disappointed as I had mentally prepared and psyched myself up for it all day but, as it had to be this way, I had to accept it. So, I didn't allow my feelings of disappointment to last too long.

I spent the day 'top and tailing' a mailshot I'd written over the weekend, adding personal bits to each recipient. I spent time in prayer and Bible study, and I did a lot of knitting. Although chemotherapy hadn't started, when I finally turned the light out on that first day, I felt I'd had a productive day nevertheless and I gave thanks to God.

Tomorrow my treatment would begin. My life would be different for ever more.

Chapter 8 – Finally it begins

'Well, God, I'm here and right now there's a distinct lack of healing happening. I'm sure that there must be a good reason why you decided not to heal me yet, known only to you, personally, of course! Anytime you would like to share your thoughts on this, you know where I am. You know I didn't want to have to go through what's about to happen as I'm a complete and utter coward when it comes to experiencing bodily excretions and pain – especially the pain part. And bodily excretions – especially being sick. Not a huge fan of vomiting, by the way. Nor, as a matter of fact, diarrhoea. Having fast, furious explosions from my bottom – I can do without that if you're in charge of that area as well. Those two are my least favourite, if you're up there listening.

'Oh yes and by the way, they say that hair is a woman's crowning glory, so losing my hair and looking like a bowling ball, isn't going to be a barrel of laughs either. There is only one woman who looked absolutely stunning without hair and that was Sinead O'Connor. I would just look like a pin head on a large body, apt to frighten furry animals and small children and, no doubt, if I lived in times where horses and carriages parked outside one's house, I'd probably make the horses bolt.

'All those prayers offered up on my behalf by so many thousands of people all over the world, God – were you busy elsewhere when they were said? You've answered my prayers before with a lot less effort on my part, I might add. Have I used up my lifetime's prayer quota, is that it? And now I have to endure what comes my way with a stoic stance and calm countenance? Is this 'the' test?!

'As you know, I'm about to have chemotherapy today, so I put myself in your Hands because you know what's best for me. I trust you to lead me through the valley of the shadow of death and, hopefully, I'll come through at the other end and everything will be OK again? Please keep my cats safe and help Steve over the next few weeks as he looks after them. I hope my cats don't forget me and, if I can just add this bit as well, God, I hope they don't freak out when they see me without any hair. They don't think humans moult! Thank you, very much. Love, Pauline.'

God to Pauline: 'Finally, I can get a word in edgeways! You had me at 'Hello!' For I know the plans I have for you, plans to prosper you, not to harm you. You may not know why you are here right now, but I know the end from the beginning. Trust me. Be still, and know that I am God, and I am always with you. Love God.'

'P.S. You'll totally rock the bowling ball look. Your cats will always love you unconditionally and be there for you ... as will all your prayer warriors and Daily Mews readers. xxx'

I sat on the edge of my bed and waited for the nurses to come and do whatever it is they had to do to start the chemotherapy. I'd had my breakfast, washed and dressed myself, and done my Bible study, and had my prayer time. This was it. This was finally it. Unless a doctor hurled himself through the door, in slow motion for better cinematic effect, to say that the blood tests taken earlier that morning had proved, beyond all shadow of doubt, that I no longer had leukaemia – that miracle of miracles – that I had been healed and God was just keeping me on my toes – then twenty-two weeks after diagnosis, I was *finally* going to start chemotherapy.

The nurse came into the room and explained what was about to happen. There were three elements to the chemotherapy; the first two take half an hour to go through the Hickman Line and the third element takes an hour. Only two out of twenty-four hours I had to spend in this room. Couldn't I have gone home each day like other people do? I never found out why I had to stay in hospital every day, for weeks on end, when other people undergoing chemotherapy arrived at the hospital, stayed for a couple of hours and then went back home again. Of course, I didn't know then (or understand) about becoming neutropenic, where I'd be open to infection, or that I'd have to wait for my neutrophils count to go back up to an acceptable level.

While the treatment was going through the Line, I sat on my bed and wrote in my journal. The only alarming side effect was when I went to the bathroom, my urine was pinkish! This was because the second element of the chemotherapy was red, and this caused a rather dramatic colour change to my urine. Nothing hurt (so far), and I could honestly say that although I had been very apprehensive about having chemotherapy, so far so good.

Some years ago, in the early 1990s I had worked for the British Medical Postgraduate Federation in London. My boss, Dr Jack Tinker, was the Dean of Postgraduate Medicine and it was his responsibility to oversee the course content for doctors in training. One of the new courses that he had been pioneering was Oncology, and it had fallen to me to gather some top Oncology doctors in the country to have a meeting with Jack at our Millman Street offices. Having produced a buffet-style lunch for these eminent minds, I had to sit in on this meeting and take the minutes.

There was one part of the meeting, when Jack turned to me and asked me if I had anything to add. I hadn't been prepared for this but, as I hadn't heard it mentioned during the meeting, I said I thought the way a patient is told they have cancer was important. Also, the way family members or carers are given the necessary resources and help in order to care for the patient, once they are back at home, was equally important. It was ironic, I thought, that I should have that input and was now a beneficiary of my own comments.

I then reflected back to June when I was diagnosed and, again, wondered why God had chosen not to heal me before I had to undergo chemotherapy treatment. I do believe that the results of all the prayers had bought me those five extra months at home; five great months where I'd been able to monitor my five remaining cats in their grief at losing Garfield.

Although I'd been devastated at losing Garfield, there had been a sense of relief because he would have wondered where I was when I finally went into hospital. He often became disorientated if he couldn't see me or if he hadn't seen me for a little while. He needed care throughout the day, which I had been only too happy to give, and after twenty years together, we were like an old married couple; I knew what he wanted when he either looked at me or meowed a certain way. It would have been nigh impossible to get someone in to look after him the way I had done. Steve was good at caring for my cats whenever I went on a two-week holiday, but Garfield had special needs, and I doubted that Steve would have been able to interpret

Garfield's needs the way I could.

Those extra five months at home also gave me the time I needed to get the house in order in readiness for Steve to 'move in' while I was in the hospital.

In the early afternoon I began to feel very sick and I thought I might have diarrhoea as well. I waited a while before pressing the buzzer to call the nurse. I told her how I felt, and she then went to fetch a doctor. The doctor asked me lots of questions and then gave me an anti-emetic (anti-sickness) drug which made me feel woozy, weird, and spaced out. Then my legs, or more specifically my knees, became restless and no matter how or where I positioned them nothing would ease the jerkiness.

I began to cry and told the doctor that this was only day one of chemotherapy and I couldn't do it for another six months. She hugged me and said they could always give me things to help with all the unwanted side effects. Thank goodness.

I just wanted to sleep but, with my legs the way they were, it was useless to even try, and I spent two hours with them going in all directions. It was as if they wanted to go to a disco while the rest of me wanted to stay in and sleep. Finally, I was able to drift into a fitful sleep and for the time being they returned to normal.

My hospital room was very basic, much like a budget hostel, but it had an en-suite shower room which was more than adequate, and quite spacious with lovely views over the visitor car parks and fields across the road.

There was a small television set, but it was impossible to get a good reception despite there being two aerials. I'd jiggle them, alternately, and get my visitors to try as well, but to no avail. I had to resort to listening to the programmes that I would have watched but it wasn't very satisfactory. Strangely, I could watch DVDs without any problems, so I watched the couple that I'd brought in with me.

The stark bare walls were relieved, in part, by a couple of tiny pictures – far too small for the room, really - which Bob had straightened up for me the previous morning. Above the door was a small clock with quite a loud tick.

This was to be my home for the next five or six weeks and although it wasn't the Ritz, what it lacked in home furnishings was more than compensated for by the wonderful nursing staff and doctors who visited me throughout the day. Their cheerful smiling faces allayed all fears and they answered any questions I had with utmost honesty – which I really appreciated.

In order to face this battle and to fight it with as much strength as I could muster, I needed to know what my enemy consisted of, what dirty tactics it was liable to use and whether I could fight – and beat – it. So, I asked a lot of questions! Knowledge is power.

My roommate was prone to sudden outbursts, fits of shuddering, long wistful sighs and the most spectacular farts. He was everything I liked in a roommate except he was very monosyllabic – in fact, he never said a word the entire length of my stay. But I conversed freely with him. Shirley Valentine had Wall; Tom Hanks had Wilson the Volleyball; I had Fridge.

We would converse on all manner of subjects and we put the ills of the world to rights. I say 'we', but Fridge was the strong silent type and, in truth, probably couldn't get a word in edgeways once I was in full flow. But, occasionally, he'd splutter incoherently or sigh sadly and I'd stop, mid-sentence, to see if he wanted to add anything further.

He introduced himself on my first night when, in the early hours of the morning, he suddenly spluttered into life, sighing as if the weight of the world was on his shoulders. The burden of keeping my yogurt safe from harmful bacteria seemed too much for him to cope with and he shuddered. With a final flurry of several succulent farts, he lapsed into silence briefly while gathering up his strength for his next outburst.

'Oh, good,' I thought, at the time, 'a Fridge with Tourette's' as he spent the next ten- or fifteen-minutes alternating between snorting, farting, sighing and shuddering.

The one thing I treasured about Fridge was his capacity to purr. Often after an outburst of spluttering, shuddering and incredible farting, he'd settle down into a rhythmic hum which eventually became the sweetest purr. Missing my cats as I did, this loving reward from Fridge, who'd put up with the one-sided rants and raves, 'If I was Prime Minister, this is what I'd do' type of conversations, was like a sweet balm to my ears. And as strange as it may seem, Fridge got me through some tough times.

Closing my eyes, I'd visualise each cat in turn, even Garfield, and I'd mentally stroke them, tell them what good boys they were, how much I loved and missed them and, Mummy would be home soon.

As soon as I closed my eyes, Fridge burst into life again before settling himself into a comforting whirr, which built up to a resonant snorty purr. Soothed, I snuggled down in my narrow bed, and let the gentle purrs lead me to sleep while I dreamed of my four beautiful ginger boys, Billy, Timmy, Ricky and Ollie, and my sleek black smoothie, Sam.

And so, a kind of repetitive monotony set in; each morning

would begin at some ungodly hour with a thermometer shoved in my mouth, and I'd stick my arm out from under the blankets so that the blood pressure cuff could be attached. I'd try not to wake up while this was going on but, inevitably, I would need to go to the bathroom. A cup of black coffee was then brought to me by one of the nursing auxiliaries and I'd sleep until breakfast arrived.

Usually, just as I was having my breakfast, or about to start eating it, a phlebotomist would come and take blood from me.

Sometimes when I had visitors, Fridge who'd remained silent for so long, would suddenly let out a humongous fart. The visitor would look at me and I would look at them, but I knew who the culprit was and would try not to laugh. Then there would be a deep sigh as Fridge tried to cough discreetly and apologise: 'Sorry about that.'

'Well, that's a relief,' I'd shrug nonchalantly and say to my visitor. 'For a minute there, I thought that was you! It's not easy sharing a room with a fridge that has such deep emotional issues,' I'd add.

Fridge would be so embarrassed that he would remain silent for as long as he could while I had visitors, but usually the excitement of them being in the room would have him shuddering, snorting, sighing, and farting in quick succession. He hadn't quite learned social skills and it was difficult for him to curb his enthusiasm when visitors arrived.

I did think I ought to explain to my unsuspecting visitors that Fridge was apt to explode now and then but having explained to one or two and Fridge not doing anything until after they had left, I decided to leave things as they were. He might have been trying his best and I'd maligned his character for nothing, upsetting his feelings, so discretion was called for.

About two weeks after I began having chemotherapy, I noticed my hair was coming out whenever I touched it or combed it. This didn't worry me unduly because I knew I would lose it. But in the third week, after I had a shower, I noticed an awful lot of hair around the drainage hole and wondered what might be left on my head. Too frightened to look, I wrapped a towel around my head, got dried and dressed, and cleaned my teeth, putting off the inevitable.

Then, having nothing left to do, I took the towel off my head and gently began to comb through my hair. It came out in great clumps in my hand, and I stood there looking in the mirror in disbelief. All I had left were a few wispy bits and lots of very bald areas. I cried my eyes out. I always said that I wouldn't cry, what would be the point? But the point was that it was me – and it felt like I was losing me.

One of the consultants came in for the usual ward round and he gasped with shock when he saw me. Only the day before I had a reasonable head of hair; now it was virtually gone. He couldn't believe how much I had lost and how quickly it had come out. I started crying again. He patted my arm but didn't know what to say, so I stopped crying to make him feel better.

I realised that crying actually wouldn't change anything. My hair was still coming out and by the next day, or the one after, in all probability, I would be utterly bald, and crying wouldn't make my hair stay where it was. The hair follicles were unlikely to band together in solidarity and say: 'This woman is upset about her hair falling out. What do you say? Let's not make any more come out! Let's do some damage limitation here!'

Chemotherapy is like Sylvester Stallone rampaging through

your body, killing everything in sight; nothing is spared until he reaches The Target! It kills all cells including hair follicle cells, so whether I liked it or not, cried or not, baldness is one of the stages.

One of the people from the local Baptist church came to see me in the afternoon. She brought me some Roses chocolates and a magazine. But I couldn't believe it. She actually had a cold. How could she even think it would be ok to visit someone in hospital with a cold? Didn't she realise the ramifications that her visit could have on me? I was neutropenic and therefore susceptible to any and all infections. Coming in my room with a cold was extremely dangerous for me.

Billy, one of the nurses, put his head round the door and asked if I was all right. I didn't have the heart (coward that I was) to tell him that my visitor had a cold, so he left. But after she'd gone, he came back to see me, I told him the truth and he went ballistic. He told me in no uncertain terms that any visitor who was unwell should not, in any circumstances, visit me because they would be putting me at serious risk. He told me that if I couldn't tell them to go, to call for a nurse and get them to tell the visitor to go. I felt guilty because it's not an easy or straightforward journey to get to Queen Mary's Hospital, and there are always road works somewhere along the route; I was grateful to see people and thankful that they had taken the trouble to come and see me.

Common-sense should have prevailed, however, and she should have waited until all traces of the cold were gone before coming to visit me. It wasn't just me that she was putting at risk; there were other people on my ward who could easily have caught the cold from her.

A couple of days later, I was woken up at just after 5 in the morning by an auxiliary nurse wanting to do my OBs. For some reason I couldn't get back to sleep, so I made myself a decaffeinated black coffee and ate the last hospital banana that was in my fruit bowl. Then I managed to go back to sleep for a few short minutes before the drugs trolley came round at 6.00.

Not long after breakfast and quite without warning, I was suddenly very sick, filling up three bowls full the first time, one and a bit bowls the second time, and a smaller amount the third time. Billy came in, dealt with it, told me not to worry and gave me some anti-emetics. One of the consultants came in to see me and suggested that I stop taking the Slow K (potassium) tablets because it can cause sickness.

Mid-morning, I was given a platelets infusion and just after lunch, when Billy was flushing the Hickman Line, it 'popped', and a coloured liquid splashed all over my stomach. He clamped the Line and then the consultant came back to have a look at it. This was Saturday and I had to wait to Monday to have it x-rayed to see if there was a blockage. This meant that I couldn't have a shower because Billy had put a dressing over the Line, and I wasn't allowed to get it wet.

That evening, one of the nurses, James, put a cannula in the back of my hand so that the intravenous antibiotics could be administered through it. I wondered how I'd be able to go to sleep with this 'thing' on the back of my hand and a lock on the Hickman Line; I had to be careful which position I slept in so that it didn't dig in my chest.

Looking out of my window the next morning as I sat up in bed drinking my early morning coffee, I couldn't believe what I was seeing. Torrential rain and severe gales. So much so, that the rain was being blown horizontally in great sheets of water. When the blood lady came in, she said that there had been some serious floods throughout the country and one of the routes she took to the hospital had such a deep mass of water, that it would have come up to the handlebars of motorbikes who were foolhardy enough to try and drive through it. The sun was shining by mid-morning and looking out, it was hard to imagine anything so destructive had occurred only a few hours previously, the flooded car parks proof of Nature's more desperate acts.

Opposite the hospital, on the other side of the road, there was some green parkland, edged with trees and shrubs. Wild parakeets perched in the trees during the day and flew about in great green clouds at any given moment, giving the dull, lead-like sky a burst of vivid colour. I often looked at the trees. One, in particular, caught my attention. As it was November, most of the trees were bare. This tree, however, had one leaf tenaciously holding on. I glanced at it several times a day over the next few weeks to check on it. To my surprise, it survived the storms, the gales, and whatever else Nature threw at it. That leaf became my visual mantra. I felt it was a symbol from God to show that he's in control and that if I hold on, put my trust in him, he won't let me go, no matter what the storms of life are taking me through.

There was a rectangular mirror in my room which was placed on the back of the door, positioned in such a way that I could see from my chest up. I could check on the Hickman Line (when it was working) and I could monitor the gradual, and then the dramatic, all-in-one-go hair loss, but I couldn't see anything below the waist. I was still being weighed on a daily basis and my weight was fairly static but, because I couldn't see my body, I imagined that I was now a sylphlike beauty. Of course, the huge Bridget Jones knickers I donned everyday told another story, but it didn't hurt to dream, did it? Dreams cost nothing.

As I probably only used a quarter of a calorie just going from one side of the bed to the other, it made perfect sense to me that my weight wasn't going to plummet from my eyebrows down, and that I'd probably have to eat considerably less, and move around considerably more for there to be any visible changes.

As I came out of the bathroom one evening, after one of my frequent visits, I noticed the beautiful, incredible full moon. The one where its features wistfully look to the right as if it's gazing at something far more interesting than anything here on Earth. Mesmerised by its fullness and ethereal beauty, I just kept staring at it and wondered if the moonwalk in 1969 was the biggest hoax in history or whether man truly did take one small step for man, one giant leap for Mankind.

Chapter 9 – Exit the Hickman Line

On the Monday, I was whisked off by wheelchair to the x-ray department to have a Linogram to see if there was a blockage with the Hickman Line somewhere. I had to wear a mask, which looked a bit odd: bald woman in a wheelchair with a mask – and I wondered if I looked like a mad old lady.

The doctor in the x-ray department was a man of few words and, despite my questions, he didn't tell me if there was any reason for the Hickman Line's failure. I was returned to the ward, none the wiser, in a wheelchair still wearing the mask, and found my lunch was waiting for me.

After lunch I had a steady run of visitors from Geoff, the vicar from my church, then a couple of other friends, and Pat, the Wig Lady. Earlier in the week, I had looked in a wig catalogue and with the help of some of the nurses, my consultant, Dr W, and my own nervous choice, had chosen three different styles of wig. Most of the wigs were given girls' names, but a few had 'encouraging' type names and one of them was 'Spark'. As I've always had short hair, one of the nurses suggested I should try a long blonde wig, but when I put it on, it looked not only scary but also horrible. I tried on 'Spark' and Pat, the Wig Lady, said it looked nice. I tried on 'Judy' which was slightly shorter, darker with highlights, but my mind was made up. 'Spark' it would be, and I put it back on again, while Pat showed me how to dress it. I hoped that before I left the hospital, my hairdresser friend, Lesley, would come and shape it for me.

Pat also showed me how to use bandanas and brought a selection in the colours I said I liked. She tied one round my head and I was surprised at how nice it looked. I tried it, but the end result made me look like a peasant woman. We laughed, and I tried again. There were many different ways to wear the scarves, and Pat said that I didn't have to wear it in the way she'd shown me if I found it difficult. She left me with the wig and an assortment of scarves. I put the wig back on again after she went out of the room but didn't really like what I saw when I looked in the mirror.

I was fortunate that I still had eyebrows and eyelashes, although a few eyelashes towards the outer corner of each eye seemed to have gone the way of the hair on my head. My body hair had also disappeared, which was a cause for concern as I didn't see it going. I mean, the hair on my head came out gradually and then there was the mass exodus that memorable morning in the shower, but other hair just went; one minute it was there and then it wasn't. It was very strange.

While I was musing on my hairless body parts, another friend of mine came to see me and we were enjoying a really good hearty talk, when Dr A and one of the SHOs came into my room and said they were going to take the Hickman Line out at that precise moment.

They told me that it would probably hurt quite a bit because for the four or five weeks that it had been in place, skin and tissue would have grown around it. Dr A mentioned to me that they would have to anaesthetise the area around the part where it exited on my right breast, but the procedure to remove it should only take about twenty minutes. Famous last words.

My friend decided not to stick around for this gruesome turn of events, and I went to the toilet to pray that God would get me through this next hiccough.

Dr A and the SHO returned to my room gowned up, pushing a metal table containing all manner of instruments of torture, necessary to perform the withdrawal of the Hickman Line.

I needed several shots of lignocaine to stop me from squealing or wriggling and then J, the SHO, had the unpleasant task of trying to find the cuff of the Hickman Line which was stopping it from just being pulled out.

An hour and several injections later, the Line was out. I had four stitches and my right bosom looked like a war zone with a lot of bruising, blood and the stitches looking like spiders' legs dangling over the edge of a precipice – as did the medical tray with all the bloodied instruments. This meant that I would have to have another Hickman Line put in sometime before I went home in the next few days. Because of this unexpected hiccough, it now looked likely that I would have to stay in another week or so. It was just as well I hadn't got my hopes up, or I would have been very disappointed.

With the constant stream of visitors throughout the day, and the kerfuffle with the Hickman Line, I realised that I hadn't been able to have a sleep at any point and suddenly I felt totally exhausted. How weird, I thought to myself, I'm in hospital where you'd think you'd be able to rest to your heart's content yet, I'd been so busy I hadn't even been able to lie on the bed and have a nap.

Since having chemotherapy my bowel habits had changed considerably. Whereas I wasn't being sick too much, I was frequenting the bathroom for reasons other than just having a wee. And some days it felt as if the world was falling out of my nether regions and, despite having regular Imodium tablets, nothing seemed to work to stem the tide as it were. Later in the day, after the evening meal had been brought round, I had an interesting discussion with Irish Mary, one of the lovely nurses who spent a lot of time with me. We had a short discourse on our individual interpretation of what constitutes a normal poo. I said sausage shaped, and Irish Mary said what I'd produced was what the guidelines recommended. At least I'm doing something by the book!

While I was settling down to sleep, one of the nurses tried to put the antibiotics into the cannula, which was in the back of my hand, and it was really painful. It had hurt earlier on in the day when Tina, another nurse, had tried to do the same thing. Now it looked as though this cannula had to come out and I'd have to have one in the back of my right hand. I knew I was in for more pain and discomfort, and I am the world's worst person when it comes to pain.

Tina came back to try and put a cannula in the back of my right hand and was unsuccessful. Now I had a huge piece of wadding and a plaster on it to stop the bleeding.

A doctor from A & E was bleeped and he said he'd come up later to try. I finally settled down to sleep at almost midnight and then at 2.30 in the morning, a doctor who looked about twelve years of age came up to try and find a vein in which to put a cannula. An abortive attempt on my right hand produced another pad and plaster but, finally, success on my left hand just below my thumb. The 'sharp scratch' made my stomach churn, and then I had to wait for Tina to come back to flush it before putting the antibiotics through it. I hoped it wouldn't hurt, and then the one on the back of my left hand could be removed.

It took almost fifteen minutes to remove it, and then I had to wait for another nurse to come as Tina was busy elsewhere on the ward. Finally, at almost 3 o'clock I had the antibiotics, the line was flushed, and I could settle down to what I hoped would be an interruption-free sleep.

I had a large pad and plaster on the back of my left hand; a large pad and plaster on the back of my right hand; another large pad and plaster on my right wrist, and I had four stitches in my right bosom. I felt like I'd been to war, who knew that hospitals could be such dangerous places.

Chapter 10 – When can I go home?

There is a basin in my room which visitors, doctors, nurses, and other assorted personnel, use before and after they've poked and prodded me. I often used it to have a wash in if I couldn't have a shower for some reason, and this particular morning was one such a time. I was in the middle of having a strip wash when the 'Hostess', who had brought breakfast earlier, knocked on the door to retrieve my empty dishes. I was half naked – with the top half of me exposed. I didn't know which part of 'Wait a minute!' sounded like 'Come in', but she just opened the door. I had nowhere to hide and not enough time to grab a towel.

She apologised and went back out of the room. I reached for the towel, which had been lying on my bed, and wrapped it around me. Then I took the tray with my breakfast dishes and opened the door where she was waiting outside. She apologised again, and I resumed my wash.

I had just finished dressing and was drying the few wispy strands of hair I had left when Alex, the cleaner, knocked on the door. At least he had the good manners to wait before barging in. He always chatted about all sorts of things unless he saw me lying on the bed trying to sleep. Then he was fairly quiet and went about his bin emptying duties very carefully.

The activities of the early part of the morning always left me exhausted, and I had just settled myself down for a mid-morning nap after the cleaner left, when J, the SHO, popped her head round the door. She came into the room to look at the 'wound' on my right breast from where the Hickman Line had been removed a few days earlier to check if it needed to be redressed. She said it was looking all right and that she would try to arrange for me to have another Hickman Line put in as soon as she could. In the meantime, another dye test had been arranged for the following morning to make sure there were no blood clots around the area where the Hickman Line had been put in.

Talk turned to the possibilities of returning home and it was tentatively suggested that once the second Hickman Line had been put in, and as long as my neutrophils count had reached the magic number five, I could probably go home a day or so later.

To say I was excited was an understatement. I had been in hospital for five weeks and was getting a little bit fed up with Shepherd's Pie three or four times a week. Being neutropenic limited the food I was able to eat for fear of infections and cross-contamination. I could eat a jacket potato for example, but I was not allowed to eat the skin. And sometimes, despite ticking my food choices each day on the menu sheet, the meals that I ended up with were not the same as what I'd ordered. Shepherd's Pie was often sent as an alternative to my own choice, and I was sick and tired of it. To this day, I feel ill at the sight of mince.

I thought about my cats every day, and I wondered if they would remember who I was or if they'd forgotten all about me. Steve had visited me every Saturday morning bringing the post that came to the house. He also took home my laundry and brought back freshly cleaned clothes on his next visit.

Finally, on Friday 15 December, I was told I could go home. Although I hadn't had the replacement Hickman Line put in, it was decided that I'd come back the following week to have it done.

Lesley, my hairdresser friend, came to the hospital to dress 'Spark', my wig. She shaved off the last few stubborn wisps of hair and put the wig on me. I hated it immediately but knew it would only be for a short while. I had been waiting in the corridor talking to Lesley before she left, when my friend, Almeric, turned up. He had come to take me and all my accumulated baggage home but walked right past me as he didn't recognise me. As it was almost lunch time, we decided to go to the Brewer's Fayre restaurant, which was near to the hospital, for something to eat.

While he was at the bar ordering our food, I waited at the table. I felt so uncomfortable in my wig. I was convinced that everyone in the room was looking in my direction and making comments behind raised hands 'that woman is wearing a wig!' I'm sure they hadn't even noticed me, but I know I would have felt less self-conscious if I had just been myself and gone 'au naturel'.

Almeric dropped me at home, and all my bags lined the hallway for me to deal with when I had the energy. Steve had already left for his own place, grateful, no doubt, that he could get back to his own routines and his familiar bits and pieces. The house was spotless; he had done a wonderful job of keeping it clean for when I returned. I didn't know what I'd be capable to doing post chemotherapy, and I was very grateful to him for keeping it so nice and tidy.

I took the wig off and put it on the dining table. None of

the cats were downstairs so I went upstairs to see if they were in my bedroom or the office, which had been Steve's bedroom for the past five weeks.

They were all lying on my bed: Billy, Timmy, Ricky, Sam and Ollie – fast asleep. Gently I spoke to them. 'Mummy's home!' Billy woke up and looked at me. I half expected him to shriek out something in Felinese 'we have a mad furless woman in the house, boys!' but he didn't. He got up and walked over to me. I picked him up and he nestled into my neck, purring fit to burst. One by one the others woke up, and all came over to me. I put Billy back on the bed, and he must have told them that the strange looking woman without any fur was Mum because they didn't react in a negative way to me not having any hair. They all clustered around me, smelling me, and putting their front paws up on my chest so I'd pick them up for cuddles. I wondered if I had a smell about me as if I'd been staying at the vets' surgery all these weeks.

We all went downstairs together, and all the various bags still lined up in the hall were subjected to intense sniffing before, satisfied that they were Mum's bits and pieces, they made their way into the kitchen. I was way ahead of them and was busy preparing a little welcome back snack although, in reality, it should have been them preparing the welcome home treat for me.

David, my son, popped in to see me on his way home from work and took a picture of me with his phone. I showed him what I looked like with the wig on, but we both agreed I looked better without it.

Later, when I was sitting on the sofa watching the television, Billy climbed on to the back of the sofa behind me and, with his paws around my neck, he gently patted my bald head. 'Don't worry,' he seemed to say, 'with or without fur, you're still the best Mum in the world.'

On the Monday I had to go to Queen Mary's Hospital for blood tests, and then I had to go back the following day to have another bone marrow test. Dr A performed it with Dr R and Katie in attendance. Despite being given sedation, it did hurt, and I hoped that I wouldn't have to have too many more in future.

Christmas came and went, and although I had received invitations to share Christmas with friends, I had to steer well clear of everyone in case I got any infections. My next-door neighbour, Paula, who had moved to another house a couple of streets away before I'd started the chemotherapy, brought me a Christmas dinner and my other neighbour, Marge, gave me a dinner on Boxing Day.

On Friday 29 December, I met Tony, my brother, and his wife, Jackie, at Victoria Station to show them where King's College Hospital was. We had to meet with the Bone Marrow co-ordinators and we both had to have lots of blood tests in readiness for the stem cell transplant which was scheduled for early January.

On January 4 Gary, my neighbour from across the road, took me to Queen Mary's Hospital. I had to have blood tests done before going to theatre to have another Hickman Line put in. When we got back home again, he cooked me pasta for my dinner. I was sick before and after eating, which wasn't a reflection of his cooking, and it was very kind of him to offer to cook for me. As I'd felt so queasy, I hadn't felt up to preparing anything for dinner.

I rarely wore my wig when going out, preferring to wear a striped beanie hat pulled low down to my ears and I surprised myself by not minding my bald status. If people knocked on my front door and they didn't know about the leukaemia, they got the shock of their lives when I opened the door and they saw my shiny bald head.

And Billy seemed fixated with it. At every opportunity he'd sit on the back of the sofa behind me when I sat watching television, and he'd pat my head. He even took to grooming me, his raspy little tongue journeying over my scalp. Perhaps he thought it would stimulate my hair growth. Far from worrying what the cats would make of me without hair, I'd been welcomed back home as if I'd never been away. Little did they know that I was about to go away again for another unknown period of time, and their lives would change once again.

Chapter 11 – Stem cell transplant time

Exactly four weeks after I left Queen Mary's Hospital my new next-door neighbour, Laurence, (who had moved into Paula's house) took me up to King's College Hospital on Friday 12 January 2007 in the afternoon. He is a cab driver, and as it was on the way to where he worked, he didn't mind taking me. He worked at night and slept during the day, so the journey provided us with the opportunity to get to know each other as our paths were not likely to cross in normal, everyday circumstances.

King's College Hospital is in Denmark Hill, South East London and that was to be my home for the foreseeable future. Transplant Day was scheduled for Monday January 22, which was 10 days later, and the days in between would be spent having yet more chemotherapy. Oh, Great Joy!

I had to book into Davidson Ward to begin with, and I was settled into a comfortable two-bedded ward with a lovely West Indian lady, called Eileen, who was having the symptoms of her sickle cell anaemia treated. Joanna, one of the nurses, came in to take my medical history, but on seeing my bald head, exclaimed:

'Oh, my goodness, you have the perfect shaped head.'

I laughed and asked her how she came to that conclusion, and she went into details about various lumps and bumps on people's heads which made them look 'odd'. I suppose I developed a slight swagger after her comment at the thought that I had the perfect shaped head to carry off the bald look and, as strange as this may sound, it helped me not to mind about not having any hair. I didn't feel self-conscious anyway about being bald. It was other people, I noticed, that seemed uncomfortable around me when they realised that under the beanie hat which I always wore, there lurked a hairless head.

Throughout the evening, which seemed to speed by, various people came to ask me questions or to attempt to take blood from the three lumens on the Hickman Line, which wouldn't oblige. In the end, blood was taken from the vein in my right arm.

At 11.30pm just as I was considering going to sleep, (having been up since 7 that morning), a nurse came in with a bag of Aciclovir, an anti-viral drug, which had to be given via the Hickman Line. I was so tired, but it had to be given in preparation for the chemotherapy which was due to start the following morning. Groaning, I sat up in bed while it went through the line.

It took just under an hour and then the line had to be flushed, which took another twenty minutes. Fortunately, Eileen was awake, so we were chatting. Earlier in the evening after the dinner had been brought in, she said she was going to have a little sleep so that she could watch a particular programme on television. Bless her - she slept right through her programme as well so, at her 'usual' bedtime, she wasn't sleepy. So, she kept me company while the Aciclovir was going through the Hickman.

It was in the early hours of the morning before we both settled down to sleep, but it took me ages to drift off, and I kept waking up at the slightest sound. What neither of us heard – which surprised us as we're both very light sleepers – was that someone came in our room at some point and wheeled away the stand that had been used for the Aciclovir to drip through, to use for another patient.

No sooner had we got to sleep than it seemed as if we were being woken up again to have our OBs done, and shortly after that, a nurse arrived to give me another bag of Aciclovir. As the stand had gone missing, she had to hunt around for it, which delayed its start.

Chemotherapy was due to start mid-morning, but finally started just before lunch. It only took about thirty minutes, which wasn't too bad, and then the line was flushed. I was told that I'd be going into the Derek Mitchell Unit as soon as I'd finished the chemotherapy. This would then be my home for the next four – six weeks. So, God put Eileen and I together for a reason. It was her last night after a two week stay, and my first night of a stay lasting several weeks. It was great that I had such a nice person with which to begin my journey; she had prayed for God to send her someone nice and a Christian to be her roommate. And she got me!

Eileen left later in the afternoon and I moved over to the Unit just after dinner. I was pleased to find that I had a reasonably good-sized room, probably slightly larger than my room at Queen Mary's Hospital. There was a nice wardrobe with a hanging section, a drawer where I put my underwear and a cupboard with two shelves: one for my tops and one for my night dresses.

The en-suite bathroom was smaller but very clean. It had a shower cubicle, a toilet and a basin, and there was also a basin in my room.

There was no television, as in my previous room, but as I

only watched one or two programmes an evening, sometimes none at all, it didn't really matter. I didn't want to pay £2.00 a day to rent a television. If I stayed for the full six weeks that would cost me £84, which I thought was excessive. And probably, just to get my money's worth, I would end up watching all the rubbish as well.

Earlier in the day I had finished reading a funny book called 'Pelican Crossing' by Hilary Cotterill, about her 'misadventures' while training to be a nurse, and I'd mentioned it to Joanna the previous evening while she was taking my medical history. While discussing it with Joanna, I just knew that I was to give her the book when I'd finished reading it, so I waited until she'd be back on night duty. I walked the short distance down the corridor to Davidson Ward and gave it to her. She was quite taken aback and said no one had given her a present before, and she said if she hadn't been so tired, she'd probably start crying. I just responded by saying that it was probably better than chocolate, and she agreed.

While having my third lot of Aciclovir of the day, later that night at 10.45pm I finished reading my second book. I was concerned that I would have read all the books I had brought with me before too long, and then what would I do for the rest of the five and a half weeks that were left?

Hawkins, one of the male nurses who came in mid-morning to do my OBs, remarked about the lack of a television in my room. I told him that I couldn't afford to pay for a television for the length of time I would probably be in the hospital. He nodded, understanding. He said he'd have a look around to see if he could find one for me and, sure enough, came back while I was eating my lunch with a small portable television.

It had seen better days; there was no remote and the aerial had been mended with sticky tape, but I managed to watch the last hour of the film 'The Legend of Bagger Vance', the news and a repeat programme on tornadoes in Britain. The picture wasn't great, but better than the television I had used in Queen Mary's Hospital. But still, it was something else to while away the time if I got fed up with knitting, reading or writing.

Another thing I had to do was to keep an input and output chart. The amount I drank went into one column under the appropriate time, and my urine had to be measured and the amount written up in another column. Aciclovir infusions and saline flushes were also added, and the reasoning behind it was to ensure that my body was able to flush out what ever went in. I was weighed twice a day as well which was another way of keeping tabs on things.

I had noticed something though. When I was having chemo-therapy at Queen Mary's Hospital, I weighed thirteen stone five pounds (eighty-five kilos), now I weighed twelve stone six pounds (seventy-nine kilos) – not a huge difference, but I was pleased. It wasn't through being ill, either. But for some months I'd cut out all sweets and sugary snacks, as I had been told that cancer feeds on sugar and upped my intake of fresh fruit and vegetables. It wasn't that I was particularly more mobile, although, once I'd got my confidence after coming home from Queen Mary's, I frequently walked to the local shops to do various errands. As the weather was usually quite windy on these excursions, I didn't wear my wig in case it blew away! Instead I wore my beanie hat pulled down as far over my head and ears as possible to help keep the cold out.

I always felt invigorated after these walks, and quite 'saintly'.

But I nearly always needed a sleep once I got back home again, as any activity exhausted me. I'd sleep for a couple of hours at a time when the cats usually gathered around me to keep me company, their purring a good soothing balm to my ears.

So, I just put the gradual weight loss down to the fact that I was eating smaller portions and I wasn't eating junk or rubbish food, or any sweets (confectionary) or desserts. As my recommended weight was between nine stone six pounds – ten stone three pounds (sixty - sixty-five kilos) I knew I had a long road to travel, but had already been told by my own doctor and the consultants not to worry about dieting while I was having treatment for the leukaemia, as it would stress my body further. By not eating sweet foods, I wasn't particularly enduring great hardship – after a while, I really didn't miss eating them – but it was making a slow, but gentle difference to my weight. I was hopeful and optimistic that over time I might eventually get to my target weight.

For a little while now, I had been sporting a fuzz-like growth all over my head. Never obsessed with my hair before the way that some girls or women are, forever playing with strands of their hair or constantly pushing their fingers through it, I now found myself running the flat of my hand over it, marvelling at the feel of it. It reminded me of the texture of Action Man's hair! It was less than half a centimetre long then, but I wondered if even that would disappear again while I was having this course of chemotherapy. I had brought my wig to hospital with me but after ten minutes, I had to take it off – it made me itch.

Wearing the wig made me feel more self-conscious. My hair (when it is in its rightful place on my head and not languishing in the plug hole of the shower cubicle) is naturally very curly, so I've always worn it short; well, to be honest, it doesn't grow long in the conventional sense; it just grows outwards, in a kind of lesser Afro style. I thought that a longer length, wavy-styled wig would look good on me, but despite my hairdresser friend, Lesley, shaping and trimming it for me, it always seemed weird when I put it on, and I felt that I looked like a pasty-faced drag queen.

Chapter 12 – And so it drags on

The days wore on in a kind of boring repetition of their predecessor. I'd be woken at what always seemed to be the crack of dawn to have my OBs done. A nurse would put the blood pressure cuff on my arm and squeeze the living daylights out of it, a clip would be fastened to my finger to gauge my oxygen levels, and which ever ear was showing upwards would have the thermometer thing thrust down it until it 'pinged'.

I was particularly tired one morning, because it had been past midnight the previous evening when I finally got settled after the third batch of Aciclovir had been administered for the day. So, I was not best pleased when a nurse put the lights on at just past 7.00am wanting to do my OBs. I was happy to stick an arm out while she wrapped the cuff around it in order to take my blood pressure; I was happy enough to stick a finger out from the other hand for the oxygen levels to be monitored; but when she dragged the scales over and said: 'Right, now let's weigh you!' I was not happy.

I had to get out of my cosy bed to stand on the scales and then she just said 'Hmm' and went out of the room. I didn't know if 'Hmm' meant I had lost weight or if it was a 'Hmm' because I'd put on weight. The 'Hmm' was never explained to me.

I got back into bed and slept until the next interruption which was when the phlebotomist came into my room wanting to take blood. I had a bit more sleep, then another nurse came in to rig me up for another infusion of Aciclovir. Breakfast arrived shortly thereafter, followed by the cleaner. No peace for the wicked, it seemed.

Suddenly, all the flurry of activity died down, once the chemotherapy had been administered, and I looked at the clock and saw that it was almost lunch time. Where had the morning gone? There had been so much going on that I hadn't had time to get showered so it would have to wait now, until after lunch.

Although the doctors had done their rounds earlier, Professor M was due to see me and the rest of the patients in the Derek Mitchell Unit that afternoon, so the doctors came round again. Prof M, who was head of the Haematology Department, was a very nice man, seemingly well-liked and respected by staff and patients alike. When he called in to see me, I was cutting stamps off envelopes from letters I had received, as I collected them to send to an animal charity.

Seeing me wield the nail scissors snipping around the edges of each stamp, Prof M issued a warning to take care and not cut myself. I hadn't given much thought to the dangerous pastime that I was engaged in. I was fifty-six and had been managing scissors for as long as I could remember, graduating from the round tipped ones while I was still in infant school – what dangers could there be in cutting stamps off an envelope?

In my ignorance of all things to do with leukaemia, and the side effects that come with having chemotherapy, I did not know that getting infections at the drop of a hat (or the careless snip of a pair of scissors) are fairly commonplace and sensible precautions are necessary to avoid this. So, I smiled at Prof and told him I would be extra vigilant in my use. Actually, although I didn't realise it at the time, any infection carried via the blood – such as in a cut on a finger – could have proved fatal, and though I made light of it at the time, I realised fairly soon after Prof's departure from my room, that he wasn't being silly in his gentle advice. He was protecting me from a potentially serious situation.

Later that day I received an email from a friend in America. We subscribe to receive each other's newsletters; she has a website on Irish customs and culture, and she signed up to mine because she likes cats. Her email had a cartoon picture of a woman with a cat lying on the top of the computer monitor, and it made me smile. I placed this same picture at the top of the page on my website, and it never failed to give me a positive tingle. I don't know how she got it to me. She must have sent it to King's College Hospital main email address, which probably could be found on their website, and somehow it found me. I'm glad it did because it was very heartening and encouraging.

I also received a card from a friend that I used to work with when I worked at English Heritage in London. It had a little cat on the front sitting between the uprights of an arch with roses growing round it – a sign of normality to come, perhaps? Knowing I had ginger cats, my friend always tried to get cards depicting ginger cats, and this card didn't disappoint. But it did make me think about my own little ginger guys, and Sam, who although black, was an honorary ginger cat. I wondered how they were doing and whether or not they missed me.

My friend, Brenda, from church had sent me a text to say that everyone was praying for me but that our vicar, Geoff, was still unwell. He had been hoping to come up and visit me and that would be something for me to look forward to when he was better. I always enjoyed our conversations as he was such a down to earth person, very easy to talk to and totally non-judgemental.

I was in the middle of a big session with Mel, my nurse for the day, and Olga, who was shadowing him, when one of the subscribers to my Mewsletter, Jared, who lives in Belgium, rang me on my mobile. He said it was good to hear my voice so strong. I told him that I was doing all right – which, I was, all things considered – and that I looked like GI Jane at that moment. He told me that he was going away on business for a week and that he'd contact me on his return. He was a very caring man who also liked cats, and it was nice to know that people outside of my own little circle were thinking about me and cared enough to contact me.

The surprise email, Jared's unexpected phone call, my friend's card and Brenda's text, put a smile on my face for the rest of the day. Living in just a room with few, if any, outside visitors, it was easy to get down and depressed. I relied heavily on the constant stream of people who came into my room to do their designated tasks to fill me in on what was going on in the outside world. These little pockets of conversation, however brief, brought highlights to what were, essentially, long, tedious days of abject monotony.

There were times when I doubted that God was there. How could he let me go through all this awful stuff; how was I supposed to remain positive, upbeat and dignified when my body was letting me down in all areas? I hated not being in control and now I had absolutely no control over what was happening to me, and how my body was reacting.

I remembered a situation that Ollie (my little ginger rescue cat) had found himself in the previous summer. He'd been sitting on the gate post in the back garden one bright and sunny Saturday morning, minding his own business as he watched the world scurry by. He noticed that there was a magpie also sitting on the gate post, just a little way along from him.

The magpie began squawking at Ollie, but Ollie held his ground. It was *his* gate post, after all, and he wasn't going to let any old magpie get the better of him. The magpie's squawking intensified to such a volume, that neighbours came out of their back doors to see where the noise was coming from. Seeing Ollie and the magpie in a 'high noon' situation, they just laughed and said knowingly: 'Oh, it's only Ollie. He'll sort out that bullying magpie.' But if Ollie was scared, he didn't show it, and he crouched low to the magpie's haughty height. The magpie was actually a lot bigger than Ollie and when a second magpie flew in as reinforcement to the first one, I think Ollie was quite unnerved. But he brazened it out. They both squawked and shrieked at him. He crouched even lower and, eventually, both magpies flew off.

What Ollie's encounter with the magpies showed me was that although he was technically the hunter and they were the prey, they were a lot bigger than he was. One was bad enough, but two were powerful and frightening. Ollie was, effectively, being bullied. What is remarkable is that he stood his ground and even if he was frightened, he certainly didn't show it.

What this little vignette taught me at that time, while I was in hospital, was that I was vulnerable and, in a way, I was being bullied. I had to have all these various transfusions throughout the day and night; I had absolutely no choice and the nurses were just doing their job. And their job was to get me well again. So, in my darkest moments, I remembered

Ollie's bravery and how he stood his ground; and it did give me a strength that, at times, I felt I lacked.

Another situation which also came to mind concerned Timmy. He had been in the garden and found a baby bird that couldn't fly. It might have tried to fly, and lost its confidence or been injured, and had attracted Timmy's attention. While Timmy followed the baby as it tried to half walk, half fly along the border by the fence, Timmy was suddenly attacked by Daddy Bird. Flying low and squawking fit to wake the dead, Timmy cowered in fear under the Mexican orange bush. Mummy Bird joined Daddy and the pair of them took it in turns to dive bomb Timmy while he crouched as low as he could to protect himself.

This dive bombing went on for a while and enabled the baby bird to continue its wobbly journey away from Timmy; it found a hiding place under another bush. I went out in the garden to see what all the noise was about and saw Timmy at the mercy of the parent birds. Relief spread over Timmy's face as I went to pick him up. He nestled his head under my chin, and I held him close to me.

We both thought that that was the end of the matter. But several hours later when Timmy was about to go through to cat flap to the garden, the Daddy Bird swooped in like a jet plane as soon as his head appeared out the cat flap. Timmy quickly brought his head back into the safety of the kitchen. I didn't believe it at the time that the Daddy Bird would remember Timmy after a time lapse of quite a few hours. He allowed Billy, Sam, Ricky and Ollie to go through the cat flap unheeded, but he had Timmy's name and number and he wasn't going to let him forget what he'd done to their precious baby.

Timmy hadn't actually done anything to the baby bird. I don't know if his intentions were honourable or otherwise. To my knowledge, he'd never caught a bird or a mouse – he left that to the other cats – and he had a very caring nature. After all, he'd spent two or three years as Garfield's carer. Seeing a vulnerable baby bird may have stirred the protective side of him, as he'd been with Garfield, and I don't think he would have intentionally hurt the baby bird. Of course, Daddy Bird didn't know that!

Now this image came to mind and I can see both sides of the story. Timmy is a cat and as much as I hate it, cats do hunt birds and mice and, although he hadn't done anything at the time – he was investigating the baby bird, he told me later – the parents were quick to protect their baby from a perceived threat. For the rest of that day and the following day, Timmy was earmarked for attack every time he tried to go through the cat flap. I did look for the baby bird but couldn't find it and, as it probably couldn't fly, sadly its fate was fairly obvious.

Timmy could have given up and decide never to go in the garden again in case he was attacked, but he persevered and eventually the parents stopped grieving for their lost baby and left Timmy alone. He didn't give up, although he was very wary when putting his head through the cat flap for a while, but he knew what he wanted to do, and he did it. That was the message I felt I was getting as I laid on my hospital bed waiting as Mel was about to hook me up again for yet another transfusion of Aciclovir.

I was temporarily reprieved from this next session of Aciclovir when a porter arrived to take me for a chest x-ray. The x-ray department was down one flight of stairs on the first floor. I had to wear a mask (so that I wouldn't catch any germs) and was wrapped in a blanket to keep warm. The room I was in was kept at a constant temperature and leaving it for any reason meant I had to take very strict precautions to guard against getting any chills, or germs or infections. Just a trip in the lift was quite a perilous thing, a fact I really didn't understand at the time.

Shane, the radiographer, came from Australia and I told him that I have an aunt and a whole batch of cousins living there. He asked where my aunt lived and I told him 'Temora', which is in New South Wales, and he told me that he went to university there! Talk about a very small world.

Shane noticed my bald head and I told him that I used a specific shampoo called 'Wash and Go'; I washed my hair and it was gone! He laughed with me and while taking the x-rays, we chatted and laughed. Wishing me a quick and complete recovery, he called a porter and I was whisked back to my room, once again wearing the mask and wrapped in the blanket.

After supper I searched the television guide but there wasn't anything I wanted to watch, so I thought I'd listen to a tape. I searched high and low through all my bags, but I couldn't find the one thing I needed to be able to listen to the tapes – the batteries. I was certain I had packed them, but (like my face cloths which I had also forgotten) I must have been side-tracked at the time I was packing the Walkman and the CD player.

I went out to the nurses' station and asked one of the nurses if she could rustle me up some batteries. She said she would either get them shortly or I'd have to wait until morning. While I was standing talking to her, an overwhelming tiredness suddenly came over me and all I felt like doing was sleeping.

If I did sleep for an hour though, would it affect my ability to sleep later? I preferred to sleep well at night, but I knew it wouldn't be an early night because the Aciclovir would probably be given late because of the time the second dose had finally been administered.

I apologised to the nurse and said I had to go and lie down. She helped me to my room, and I laid on the bed for a while. I decided to do some knitting, so I got my knitting bag out of the cupboard, and there, at the bottom of the bag were the two batteries! I put them into the Walkman and listened to two tapes from the Christmas services held at my church.

I love Christmas carols and I sang along to each one. Fortunately for me, I was out of hospital in time for Christmas, but it was suggested that although I could go out, as long as I exercised caution, it would be better not to go to places where a lot of people gathered – and sadly for me, this ruled out going to church. I did miss being part of the 'Family', and I was grateful in being able to listen to the tapes so that I could take part by myself in my room. Listening to the sermon, the prayers, and the Bible Readings, helped me to focus and my faith would rise, and I'd feel stronger again. Then I'd spend some time in prayer seeking God's forgiveness for doubting him and thanking him for all these experiences which were shaping my character. The Bible tells us that God knows the beginning and the end, and I just had to put my complete faith and trust in him – just as I had to accept the doctors and nurses were doing their best for me.

Chapter 13 – Are we nearly there yet?

I had now been in hospital for five days and each day consisted of three intravenous courses of Aciclovir, which is an anti-viral agent, and a course of chemotherapy. There were numerous other interruptions throughout each day as the cleaner came and went, as did various doctors and nurses, hooking me up to different transfusions and the like, hot drinks and meals being brought round every few hours, and in between all that, I managed, somehow, to read, write, knit, listen to my CDs or tapes, and more importantly, to rest!

The highlight of my 'Day Five' was when my cousin, Colin, phoned me from Australia. It was such a nice surprise that it really buoyed my spirits up, especially as I had been feeling sick on and off for most of the day. I wasn't physically sick, I just felt it. And the only way I could deal with the waves of nausea, was to close my eyes and visualise something nice to take my mind off it.

As I had spent a lot of the day asleep or resting because I felt so unwell, I was very lethargic. I had begun to read a new book and, having read the first few chapters, it didn't seem to be my kind of book, so I went out into the main corridor and left it on a windowsill for someone else to read if they wanted to. I did listen to the Christmas Day service on tape from my church, and I really enjoyed it, wishing I could have been there. But I didn't do much knitting or any of my writing projects because I just didn't have the energy to want to do anything.

Despite having the television, I couldn't find anything I really wanted to watch which would take my mind off how wretched I was feeling.

I had to use Chlorhexadrine mouthwash and another one as well. Everything tasted vile, so that whatever I tried to eat or drink, I didn't enjoy it. Even my favourite cappuccino sachets had lost their appeal, tasting metallic and odd.

One downside to this day, which had begun so well with Colin's uplifting phone call, was that the third bag of Aciclovir hadn't been administered by the time I was settling down to sleep. It was after midnight and I thought I'd been forgotten. But eventually, Jeanette, my nurse for the day, brought it in and despite my protests at how late it was and how tired I was, it went ahead. Afterwards, the Hickman Line had to be flushed out which took another fifteen minutes, so it was well past 2.00 in the morning before I could really settle down to sleep.

The only upside (if one can call it that) to come out of the previous night's very late administering of the Aciclovir was that I was left to sleep until the dizzyingly later time of 7.30 before my OBs were taken. I kept falling back to sleep while people like Abraham, who cleaned the rooms, came in and removed the rubbish. Abraham could see I was very tired and turned the lights off again after he'd emptied the two bins in the room and bathroom.

All too soon, the first bag of Aciclovir was being hooked up and breakfast arrived not long afterwards. After I'd eaten, I slept until the next interruption.

Another cat-loving friend, Mary, popped in mid-morning. I was still in bed, waiting to be unhooked from the Aciclovir and waiting to have the Fludarubin (the chemotherapy) go through the Hickman Line. It was nice to see her, and we chatted briefly, her unexpected arrival cheering me up immensely. She nipped down to the shop on the ground floor to get me a couple of bananas before she left. For some reason, I craved bananas almost every day, which was very strange. I liked them under normal circumstances anyway, but now I really wanted them, and when I wanted one, I had to have it straight away – regardless of the time or even if it was day or night! As I had to have potassium transfusions on a regular basis, I did wonder if this craving was connected in anyway with that.

Mary couldn't stay very long visiting me, as she was at the hospital for other reasons, but had just called in to see me on the off chance. Visiting hours were from 2 – 8 pm, but the nurses turned a blind eye if someone arrived outside of those hours. The only time which was sacrosanct was the lunch period 12 – 1.30, and that was 'protected' time, so no visitors were allowed while patients ate their lunch.

From the word go, my Hickman Line had stubbornly refused to allow blood to be taken from it, and although I didn't mind, blood was always taken from the veins in my arms. I had juicy fat veins, in the crook of each arm, but it went against the nursing protocol to not use the Hickman Line for its main purpose – that of drawing blood. So, a Linogram had been booked for Friday at 11.00am and hopefully it would give an answer to the puzzle.

But I was anxious as the next day a different chemotherapy was being started and each dose would take two hours to go through the Line. It would start at 5.00am and there would be another three doses throughout the day for the next two days. The 11.00am dose on Friday would have to wait until I got back from x-ray after having the Linogram.

The next couple of days were horrendous as the side-effects from having chemotherapy four times a day kicked in. I felt so ill that I could barely get out of bed except to use the bathroom. Invariably I would be hooked up to something and somehow – goodness knows how – I managed to wheel the stand to the bathroom door, try to prop it open, while I manoeuvred myself through it, then drag the stand behind me, careful not to get the tubes snagged up or caught in the door.

Going to the toilet was something that took a great deal of effort, as one arm would be holding on to the stand for support as I felt so weak – not that it would have held me if I started to fall. And I had to wash my hands with special antibacterial soap. I had to renegotiate the door of the bathroom to get back out again, dragging the stand behind me, ensuring the tubes weren't getting snarled up or caught in its wheels and then I'd fall back into bed, absolutely exhausted, dreading the next time I needed to go to the toilet.

I didn't even have the energy to get showered or dressed; I just about managed to clean my teeth at the basin in my room. It was an effort to do anything, so I stayed in my nightdress, unable to even contemplate putting something different on.

Psychologically, I felt it was important to distinguish night from day whilst in hospital. The hospital day is a very long one and I'd taken some large tee shirts which needed to be baggy so that the nurses could access the Hickman Line with ease. These, I teamed with a few co-ordinating leisure 'bottoms', so I had a range of different coloured combinations. Wearing pretty colours helped me to not only feel feminine but wearing something clean each day lifted my spirits.

During this trying time, I was so weak I couldn't even summon up the strength to get out of bed to let the nurses make it up with fresh sheets. Fortunately, this was one time they did let me have my own way, but after three days, I managed to crawl out of bed, and finally got washed and dressed while two nurses gave my bed a thorough clean and put fresh sheets on. It took so much effort that I promptly fell back onto the bed, exhausted.

I lay in bed, hooked up to the chemotherapy, drugs for this and drugs for that, and slept on and off. As these treatments continued throughout the night I was always being disturbed, so of course, the following day I would want to sleep more and more.

While lying in bed, it did cross my mind occasionally that I might not come through this journey. I wondered about my sons and grandchildren, in what direction their lives would go, and how awful it would be if I couldn't share their experiences and adventures. I worried what would happen to my five cats if I didn't make it. I didn't want them split up as they'd always been together and got on so well as a feline family, but for them to be re-homed successfully, such might have to be the case. Unfortunately, not many people would take on five cats all at once.

There were several dark moments when I didn't think I could go on and, more than once, I called out to God to ask if he was busy perhaps, or having an off day, or had he forgotten all about me. But I don't know what drove me on or inspired me, what encouraged or motivated me to not give up. Some kind of inner purpose, maybe, I don't know. But I just felt that, despite my weakness and how awful everything was at that moment, things *were* going to improve, and I would get better. I couldn't believe that I was going through all this for nothing. To have nothing at the end of it seemed pointless somehow. After all, people around the world had been praying for me since I was first diagnosed in June 2006 and hadn't wanted to go through the rigours of chemotherapy. If there was a reason why I had to do so, then I decided that God was definitely in control of everything, and I just had to sit tight, trust in him, and keep the faith.

A phrase that I had read somewhere attributed to a recluse called Mother Julian of Norwich, frequently came into my mind when I felt down: '… All shall be well, and all shall be well, and all manner of thing shall be well', which she claimed was given to her by God himself when she was very ill and not expected to live. She recovered and believed that God had healed her of her illness. Another phrase was 'And this too, shall pass.' So, armed with my mantras I tried very hard to remain optimistic and positive in the hope that all these unwanted side-effects would, indeed, pass.

My temperature at this time was all over the place and one day it spiked at thirty-nine degrees. I was put on intravenous antibiotics and sent for a chest x-ray. The porters always went at a very fast pace as they transported me in a wheelchair to whichever department I was headed, and as it was cold rushing down the corridors at a rate of knots, I wore a bandana to keep my bald head warm, and to help protect me from picking up 'germs' I had to wear a face mask. I felt a bit like Butch Cassidy or the Sundance Kid and, when I arrived at the x-ray reception desk, wanted to announce: 'Esto es un robo. !Arriba las manos!' (This is a robbery. Put your hands up!)

Someone suggested that sucking on Calippo lollies would make my mouth feel better. It wasn't sore at this point, but it always felt dry and tepid tap water just didn't do the trick. The same nurse said I might like lemonade or Coke, but I just chose Sprite as I'm not really a fizzy drink person, and although the bubbles got me in the back of the throat, it was strangely refreshing. Two more things to add to the shopping list when I got home, I thought to myself.

Another worrying thing (for me at any rate), was that my appetite had gone out of the window. With being sick so much, all I could cope with was a mouthful of cornflakes for breakfast and maybe a few mouthfuls of either hot water or black coffee.

For lunch and supper all I could manage was cup-a-soup and a yogurt, and I'd be full up. I'd supplement my lack of food during the day – if I felt up to it – by drinking Sprite in scary bubbling mouthfuls and sucking an orange flavoured Calippo. Occasionally, I'd drink a kind of milk shake called 'Fortisip' which is a food supplement drink fortified with lots of different vitamins and minerals. I preferred the chocolate flavour as it reminded me of holidays in Spain and Greece when my sons and I had drunk copious bottles of their chocolate drink. Fortisip, having the same sort of flavour, conjured up images of happier times.

Chapter 14 – Transplant time!

Finally, after ten days of umpteen bags of Aciclovir being pumped into my body, and endless amounts of chemotherapy clearing out any leukaemic cells left in my blood, the day had dawned. This was it – Transplant Day.

It was an equally momentous day for Tony. Neither of us had been in this situation before and we hoped we never would find ourselves in this situation again. I was really overjoyed to see them when Tony and Jackie popped in at 9.30-ish, before he had to go back to Guthrie Wing to begin his four or five-hour ordeal of having his stem cells collected. Jackie had twisted her knee and was limping. She was in a lot of pain and discomfort, and needed to use a stick to help her walk, but had come as support for Tony

I was in the process of being rigged up to my usual two or three different infusions: one was the anti-viral, Aciclovir, and another was an antibiotic and the third was a potassium drip or something, which took ten hours to go through the Hickman Line.

I didn't feel great, but I didn't want them to see me so low, so I tried to rally myself a bit, and we had a good laugh. True to form, Tony took one look at me and said that, without hair, I resembled a well-polished ten pin bowling ball with big dark eyes and a mouth as the three holes. Ha, ha, Tony – nice one! I can count on my brother to not only laugh at me but make me laugh – and I mentally thanked my lucky stars that they were both there as the past few days had been hell.

Of us four siblings, Ken, Tony, Garry and myself, Tony, who was four years younger than me, was the lucky one when it came to looks etc. The Gene gods, having bypassed Ken and I in favour of Tony, had smiled on him from a great height and bestowed on him a great physique, which prior to getting CFS, he had honed to perfection after spending hours in the gym. He had our mother's small, finely boned face with large dark brown eyes. He had 'normal' hair, whereas Ken and I had been cursed with the tight wiry hair, prone to becoming frizzy when damp or wet, (in my case at least) which was inherited from our father's side of the family. At eleven years younger than me, Garry didn't do too badly in the looks department either and he had 'normal' hair, too.

Tony really was an Adonis, a pin up star, and it was such a tragedy that he'd lost his job after being off work for so long, unable to work because of the CFS. I'm sure that he often got depressed at the thought that, as the man of the household, he wasn't able to be the 'family breadwinner', so to speak. He later acquired a beautiful white, Siberian husky dog that he named Tehya, and his life improved dramatically when he took her out for walks because people would stop and speak to him. He missed the interaction of being with people that he had experienced when at work, and with Jackie and their two sons also out of the house all day, he was lonely – that is, until Tehya arrived and changed his life.

All four of us are very creative but my three brothers are exceptionally good at photography, with Tony edging to the front, perhaps, with his stunning pictures. Ken loved the outdoors and he painted incredibly beautiful pictures of wildlife. It truly broke our hearts when, in October 2002, he had dropped down dead without any warning, just three days before his fiftieth birthday.

Tony had been given a timeline by the nursing staff, which meant they couldn't stay long and chat, so after a short while they left to try and find their way back to Guthrie Wing. I managed to catch a few bars of sleep in-between all the other comings and goings, drips being checked, temperatures taken, drinks brought in, room being cleaned and so on.

I was surprised when quite early in the afternoon Tony and Jackie came back, having finished in a much shorter time span than originally expected, and we had another cheerful forty or so minutes before they had to go back again to see the co-ordinator. He didn't seem any the worse for having his stem cells removed, although I could see the tiredness etched on his face.

Carly, my nurse for the day, brought the bag of stem cells in and I kept looking at it, thinking to myself that I'd wished I'd chosen a different flavoured soup for my dinner that night, because it was the same colour as the bag of stem cells.

I also remember thinking to myself what an anti-climax it all was. That tiny bag of what looked suspiciously like oxtail soup, had such an important role to play. It came without a trumpet heralding its arrival. Unlike an organ, carried as precious cargo in a container ready to be transplanted into the recipient, without fanfare or fuss, it was hooked up to the IV stand, and slowly dripped through the Hickman Line. My future was happening in slow motion. My life was in its hands.

All that I had endured for so long now just for a bag of brownish-red 'stuff' which was supposed to save my life. It wasn't a huge bag either – quite small, really considering the important job it had to do. Could such a small amount of 'stuff' really save my life? I would have to wait patiently and pray fervently that Tony was, indeed, my life saver.

Tony's day, however, had been far more eventful than my own, beginning with a three-train journey, taking almost two hours in total, from where he lived in Enfield, Middlesex, to King's College Hospital. Four days prior, he had to have two injections a day to stimulate the growth of the bone marrow, which caused it to swell slightly. This resulted in aches and pains everywhere, and Tony said the pain in his legs, feet, and chest had been unbearable.

As he tried to climb the two dozen stairs to get to the train platform, he said that he was tempted to return home as he felt so unwell. Tony thought, at the time, that the pain in his joints and muscles were just part of the Chronic Fatigue Syndrome. He felt sick as well, which could have been down to nerves and anxiety at what lay ahead, but as that was also symptomatic of CFS, he didn't think too much about it.

Knowing that today was Transplant Day for me, he fought through the pain and continued the slow ascent to the platform just as the train pulled into the station. When he sat down in the train, he had terrible cramp in his feet. He was nearly driven to tears, too, with the pain throughout his entire body, the like of which he had never experienced before, and didn't want to experience again.

They arrived at the Apheresis Department just before 9.00am and met with Liz Tatum, a lovely, bubbly specialist nurse who was going to perform the stem cell removal on him. Having asked Tony how he felt, she was pleased when he told her that he was experiencing additional pain. She told him that was what they wanted to hear as it meant the injections had done their job. Having the pain meant that Tony's bones had expanded, making it easier for the stem cell harvesting procedure, and that was the whole point of the injections. If Tony hadn't been in any pain, he would have been given two more injections to help put him in pain and expand the bones before the harvesting could begin.

Liz put anaesthetising cream on each of Tony's arms to numb the area and told him and Jackie to go to the café for twenty minutes or so and have a cup of tea – which is when they first came in to see me. When they returned to the department, he sat in the best chair there and nearly fainted with shock when Liz stuck a huge needle in one arm and a cannula in the other. Tony told me he'd never seen a needle that big before and he'd been horrified at the thought of it going into his arm. However, the fact that it didn't hurt when it went in, meant the anaesthetising cream had done its job.

The apheresis machine uses a centrifuge to spin and separate the blood into three parts: red blood cells, white blood cells and platelets, and plasma. Blood is circulated between the apheresis machine and the bloodstream continually, being taken from the needle in one arm and returned to the cannula in the other arm. Only a small amount of blood (less than 300mls/ ½ a pint) is in the machine at any point. Up to 200mls of stem cells are collected from the white cell layer. This procedure can take between three to five hours, depending on the donor's stem cell count.

They were given sandwiches and a drink for lunch. When the procedure was finished, it was suggested that they go back to the café to get another drink while the stem cells were checked.

Tony's legs felt like lead from having sat so still for so long, but as Jackie has a fear of lifts, he managed to walk down the stairs, feeling slightly shaky and woozy. He said that standing at the top of the stairs, he became very emotional and had tears in his eyes. Whether this was because of what he had gone through or whether he realised the enormity of the situation for both of us, he wasn't sure.

He had to help Jackie down the stairs, because of her painful knee, and she had to help him because his legs were shaky. He said the picture they probably presented to others, was that of a couple of drunks, stumbling around after a good session on the booze.

A welcome and warming cup of tea and piece of cake hit the spot, and with the needle and cannula still sticking in his arms, they made their way back to the department where Liz told them that the stem cells were all right. Liz removed the needle and cannula, and dressings were applied which had to stay on for the rest of the day. Tony was amazed when he saw the needle was shaped like a boomerang when it was taken out. He had been unaware that he'd bent his arm during the procedure but, as he had been reading his book, he could have done this while turning the pages. But on its removal, Tony was again struck at how big the needle was.

For a few weeks after, Tony said that he felt unusually tired and put this down to the travelling, the day spent in the hospital and, obviously the harvesting of the stem cells. But, also, in doing this, it put extra pressure on his own body which already had its own problems courtesy of Chronic Fatigue Syndrome. I did feel bad that Tony went through all that for me, and not only just that day at the hospital, but he had to run the gamut of blood tests before it was established that he was a tissue match.

Tony had been tested for viruses which are carried in the blood, including Hepatitis B, Hepatitis C, Human Immunodeficiency virus (HIV), Human T cell lymphotropic virus (HTLV), Syphilis, and Cytomegalovirus (CMV) to see if he was fit enough to be a donor. Those tests, in addition to all the dozens of phials of blood taken on other occasions must have taken their toll on Tony. The fact that he was a tissue match and went through all that for me, and I am still alive today, is down to our bond as brother and sister.

Tony said that despite, all the fatigue he experienced, and the pain and discomfort of it all, he would do it all again in a heartbeat if he had to. The flip side of this is that I probably wouldn't be here now if he hadn't been a tissue match. The initial search on the bone marrow register hadn't produced any matches, so I will always be eternally grateful to Tony for his sacrifice and his selfless act of brotherly love.

Chapter 15 – Remind me again, whose idea was it that I should have stem cells ...?

It seems strange now, looking back in hindsight, that so much importance was placed on the power of the stem cells transplant. I wished I'd known at the time just what a really tough road lay ahead of me because I might have elected to not go through with it. Almost immediately after the transfusion I became very sick. Quite naturally my body recognised that there was an intruder in its midst and decided to eject as quickly as possible, all evidence and signs of this intruder. This manifested itself in the most abominable bouts of diarrhoea; I became incontinent from my rear end and needed giant Pampers type nappies to 'catch the outpouring' - if you'll pardon my graphic description.

I can honestly say that life was pure hell for a couple of weeks after the transfusion. If I tried to move in bed to get slightly more comfortable, then I'd have an accident in the Pampers pad; if I tried to get out of bed, I never made it safely to the bathroom without another accident occurring. Life was not good, and certainly not fun. After a couple of days of feeling decidedly crap, I burst into tears after yet another mammoth clearing up session. A nurse came in at that moment to hook me up to something which was to take hours to go through the Hickman Line, and she noticed that I was crying.

The nurses were always very busy and usually had little time to chat. They would talk while handing out pills or when they were fixing up a transfusion of some kind, but that was it – there was no time for them to just come in my room and hang out for a while as they frequently had done at Queen Mary's Hospital.

'What's the matter?' the nurse asked me, 'why are you crying?'

'I'm just so fed up feeling so ill all the time,' I began to answer, blowing my nose. 'I can't stand this feeling of helplessness and not being in control of what's happening to my body.'

If I expected a comforting word or even a cuddle, I was about to be disappointed. Walking towards the door having made sure the bag was dripping at the right frequency, the nurse said over her shoulder:

'You're alive, aren't you?'

I couldn't answer that because the door had closed, ending the conversation as abruptly as it began. I felt short-changed because I would have liked to ask her how long this diarrhoea was likely to go on, and for how much longer would I continue to feel so wretched and weak. But there was never enough time to ask those kinds of questions. The nurses were always on a very tight schedule, so they rushed in, did what they came to do, and rushed out again.

So, I just had to weather this storm, just as I had weathered the others before it. I noticed that the longer I stayed in bed, the weaker I became. So, I tried to spend a bit of time each day sitting in the chair which was near to the bed. I also began to walk around the room a little each day and, although I wasn't supposed to, I would go outside of my room to the nurses' station and try and engage in a bit of conversation with whoever was there.

There was also a laundry room where it was possible to get

my clothes washed. The drier wasn't that efficient, and I had wet underwear or tee shirts hanging everywhere in my room, ready to assail an unsuspecting doctor. But in moving around, I did become slightly stronger and, once the chronic outpourings from my rear end had started to slow down somewhat, any movement I did make was not now a fraught and dangerous activity.

Much to my surprise, only two and a half weeks after my transplant, and four weeks in total of being in hospital, I was deemed well enough to go home, and the day was set for Friday 9 February. Whilst I was actually overjoyed at the thought of going back home, I was also terrified because I didn't think I was really well enough.

Steve, my friend, who had looked after the house and cats for me for the four weeks I'd been in King's, had done a brilliant job and kept the house really clean. The cats were a bit surprised to see me and it took them a little while to realise that it was me, and I was back home at long last. I think they were expecting me to be brown rather than pasty white, as they were used to Steve looking after them when I went on holiday.

They hadn't freaked out when I had returned home from Queen Mary's after the chemotherapy treatment, nor when they saw that I had no hair. So, whether they all thought this was my new look, I don't know. But cats are very non-judgemental – they don't really mind what you look like as long as you feed them, and have a decent lap on which to nap, and love them, of course.

I think with one accord they all decided that I should ditch the wig, so I didn't bother to wear it when I was indoors, and they became accustomed to seeing my shiny 'perfect shaped' head. However, it was quite apparent to me that I would need help because I was far too weak to go upstairs, so I had to sleep downstairs on the sofa. What's more, I couldn't bend down to their food bowls without toppling over. I didn't know what to do for the best. I certainly didn't want to get rid of any of them, but my heart ached to make the right decisions for them.

I rang a friend from the veterinary practice where I had taken my cats for the twenty-odd years I'd had them. She ran a cattery and I asked her if she would board four of my five cats for the foreseeable future until I got stronger. She agreed and came round two days later on the Sunday. It broke my heart to say 'goodbye' after just two days of being at home, but it was clear that I couldn't look after myself properly, let alone look after five cats. So, Billy, Sam, Ricky and Ollie all went on their holidays. I decided to keep Timmy at home with me because he'd gone berserk in a cattery once before when I was having some work done on the house. I didn't think it was fair to put him through that again. Besides which, I needed some company, and looking after one cat would be much easier than looking after five. I knew Timmy would look after me the way he'd looked after Garfield.

Brenda, my friend from church, came round to see me and organised a carer to come in each morning to wash and dress me, and prepare my breakfast. Initially I intended to have Meals on Wheels, but I cancelled them after only two days as the meals made me sick. If I remembered to get some rolls out of the freezer the night before, the carer made them up for lunch for me before she left. She usually arrived around 7.30 each morning and would start preparing my breakfast while I'd be throwing up in a bucket in the living room. When I'd finished doing that, I'd go out into the dining room where she had a bowl of warm water ready on the dining table.

Timmy usually made his excuses and discreetly went into the back garden to allow me some privacy. I can honestly say that I think carers deserve a medal for what they do; it's not an easy job by any stretch of the imagination, and I hated the fact that I needed someone to wash me and help me to get dressed each day. Talk about dignity. What dignity? When you're in such a vulnerable position, you have no dignity. But I had to put my shyness to one side and allow her to do her job. And I'm sure she'd seen worse than my lumps and bumps.

I would sit and eat my breakfast at the table while Kim (the carer) would make up the rolls for me. I had a thing for cheese and pickle rolls every day, and I really enjoyed them – only to throw up shortly afterwards. I threw up after everything I ate, which was a shame because the ladies of my church had organised themselves into a rota, with each one providing me with an evening meal around 6pm each night. As my appetite was virtually non-existent, I only ate tiny portions and I usually shared any meat with Timmy, because I didn't want to waste what the ladies had prepared for me.

My days were spent resting on the sofa with Timmy by my side. I'd often be asleep in the afternoons and Timmy would tap me on the shoulder, or gently stroke my face, when he heard someone coming up the path. He always knew when dinner was arriving, and he wanted me to be ready when someone knocked at the door.

I had to go to Queen Mary's twice a week for blood tests and as I don't drive, and I wasn't allowed to go by public transport, I had to use hospital transport. At first, I wasn't allowed to mix with anyone else, in case I caught anything, and if a driver came with a cold, I had to ask them to send me another driver. It all sounds very diva-ish, but I had to be careful.

On Monday 26 February I had to have a bone marrow test at King's College Hospital and as I couldn't go up by train, I had to get a taxicab there. Bone marrow tests were awful, and I dreaded going because I knew it would take up most of the day, besides being incredibly painful. It had to be done because they needed to see if Tony's stem cells were beginning to take over my body. They could also tell this by doing something called a 'chimerism' test, which is a specific blood test where the results show the percentage of cells that are Tony's and those that are mine.

And so, the days went on. I felt I was getting stronger each day. I was beginning to eat a little bit more, and I could go upstairs now without needing to sit on the stairs halfway up and rest. Timmy was the perfect carer, lying next to me on the sofa and alerting me to any visitors about to knock on the door. I'd begun to sleep upstairs, and I let him accompany me rather than leave him downstairs at night.

My new routine consisted of the carer coming each morning, twice weekly visits to Queen Mary's for blood tests, and my evening meals arriving at 6.00pm by the wonderful ladies from my church. I really thought that I was on the home stretch. Although it was far too early for Tony's stem cells to have completely taken over, I thought I had licked the leukaemia, and even though I was still throwing up after every meal, I did feel so much better in myself.

One of my subscribers, Laura, who lives in America, rang me one morning in early March. We had a great conversation and

I was laughing and joking with her, telling her how wonderful I was feeling; it was true, I was feeling stronger and I felt that everything was going really well. Less than half an hour later, my world came crashing down when I received a phone call from one of the consultants at King's College Hospital.

'There's a bed arranged for you at Queen Mary's, Pauline,' he said. 'You have a simple virus in your blood which should only take a couple of days to sort out, but you need to have some intravenous medication. Give the chemo nurses a ring and they'll tell you what you need to bring with you.'

Numb with shock, I telephoned the hospital and asked for the chemotherapy unit and spoke to one of the nurses. 'Oh, you'll only be in here for a couple of days,' she said, 'nothing to worry about. Just bring your usual bits and pieces that you'll need for a couple of days and come in as soon as you can so that we can get you rigged up to begin the meds. You'll be having a course but, once we've got the virus under control, we can probably either give you tablets to take at home, or you might have to come in daily by hospital transport to continue with it; either way, don't worry, we'll soon have you up and home again.'

As I knew Steve wouldn't be able to come over to look after Timmy for just a couple of days, I asked another neighbour if she wouldn't mind coming in to feed him. It would only be for a few days, I told Timmy, while I waited for my friend Almeric to collect me. I stroked Timmy's head and he sat on the back of the sofa watching me out of the window. Little did any of us know what lay in store for me.

Chapter 16 – A 'simple' virus?

Almeric dropped me at the hospital and I took my bag to the ward which was going to be my home for the next few days. I wasn't going into the single room with the en-suite bathroom this time, indicating the impermanence of the situation. I had to use the bathroom down the hallway which everyone on the ward used, men as well as women, and as a result, it was not very nice and smelt awful. But the little room was pleasant enough and I sat on the bed waiting for whatever was going to happen next.

Lunch happened first and I ate the food choice of the person who'd vacated the room before me. It wasn't great, but it filled a gap. I settled down to read and then was hooked up to receive something called Ganciclovir, which was another type of anti-viral treatment.

I was told I had cytomegalovirus (CMV) in my blood and that it was necessary to have Ganciclovir three times a day, by transfusion, for a couple of days. Cytomegalovirus is a common herpes virus. Many people do not know they have it because they may have no symptoms. But the virus, which remains dormant in the body, can cause complications for people with weakened immune systems, which is what I now had, thanks to chemotherapy and the transplant.

I didn't feel ill and I didn't look ill, so I was very surprised that CMV had showed up in a recent blood test. But reassured that I'd be back home again in a couple of days, and that

Timmy would be all right in the meantime, I didn't worry too much.

After twelve days I was moved out of the relative security of a single room into a six-bedded bay. The main ward was made up of several bays each consisting of six beds. This concerned me considerably and I asked the nurse, who was moving my things, if I wouldn't be vulnerable out of my little cocoon. She said that I would be vulnerable, but that I'd be all right. Trusting her, as I thought nurses knew more than I did, I readily accepted this new situation without further argument.

I was given the choice of five empty beds, one being occupied already, and chose a bed next to the window so that I could watch the comings and goings outside the hospital. It was opposite a lady who didn't speak much, despite my attempts to engage in friendly light-hearted conversation, so I gave up and concentrated on reading my book.

That evening, quite late, a young woman was put in the bed next to mine. She had a chest infection, and, within two or three days, I was coughing. Other women from all walks of life had filled the other three beds and within a day or so, they were coughing also. One woman, Margaret, who was an alcoholic, was brought in during the early hours of the morning after an apparent attempted overdose on vodka and painkillers. She made enough noise to wake the dead, and those of us that had been sound asleep were now privy to her grunts, groans and profanities. After a day or so when she just laid in the bed moaning, and generally being rude to anyone who came to see her, she perked up. She walked about the bay in her bra and knickers while she put on her makeup and wasn't in the least bit shy if anyone walked down the corridor and saw her like that.

Getting completely dressed, she went downstairs and then headed out to the fields opposite the hospital, where she joined others having a cigarette break. She did this several times a day regardless of the gentle admonishing from the nurses and doctors.

The woman who'd been in the bed opposite me on my first day on the ward, was spirited away in the early hours of the morning. I didn't hear a thing – which was amazing, as I'm such a light sleeper. So, I don't know what happened to her.

Margaret spouted on and on about the unfairness of life. She complained all the time. Especially when the machine, that the drip I was hooked up on, beeped for ages until a nurse came to unhook the Ganciclovir bag and I was free for a while. One day she had just woken up and began swearing.

'What the eff is that effing noise?' she snarled. 'Can't you stop it?' she asked me.

I pressed a button and the beeping stopped for a few short minutes before setting up again. 'Effing 'ell,' she snarled again, 'that's doing my 'ead in.'

Eventually a nurse came and took down the empty Ganciclovir bag and she called out after her: 'Why the eff do we have to listen to that effing noise all the time? We need our peace and quiet. We don't want to listen to that effing beeping all the effing time.'

The nurse came back and stood next to her bed.

'I'm so terribly sorry that the beeping of that machine is causing you such problems, Margaret,' she said. 'But Pauline is fighting a serious disease in her blood and she needs to have that medication several times a day. We needed her room for someone more unwell than she is, otherwise, she'd still be in her room. Now I'm sorry it's inconveniencing you, but perhaps if you thought of someone else rather than yourself all the time, you'd realise that Pauline is a very sick woman and rather than criticising her, it would be helpful if you were kind instead.'

The nurse looked over to me and smiled. I smiled back. Margaret growled and went under her bed covers. Three of the women in the ward were alcoholics and all of them were very grumpy individuals. Being deprived of their drug of choice probably made them this way and, as none of them tried to talk to me, I was rather left out of any conversation that went on. Sometimes they'd talk until four or five in the morning, while I'd be struggling to get to sleep, but they didn't think about anyone else but themselves. They'd spend hours and hours going round and round in circles, talking about their lives and how they needed a drink. Although I did feel sympathy for one particular woman, none of them were in the least bit interested in me, showing no kindness whatsoever.

The situation was made worse one day when I was applying face cream. One of the nurses who was doing the 'pill round' at the time with another nurse, said to me:

'You have such beautiful skin, Pauline. You really take care of it.'

'Thank you,' I replied.

Margaret looked across at me and started preening herself. 'I've had a boob job,' she told the nurses. They turned to look at her as she thrust her bra-less breasts in a skimpy top in their direction. She was quite heavily made up, and always made sure she had done her face every morning before she went outside for her first cigarette of the day.

The nurses turned back to look at me. One asked: 'How old

are you, Pauline, if you don't mind me asking?'

'I'm fifty-six,' I responded, 'I'll be fifty-seven in August.'

There was a sharp intake of breath as both nurses shook their heads in disbelief. 'You look so much younger,' one said, while the other one added, 'You have such a beautiful face, and you're a natural beauty. You could easily pass for someone in their thirties.'

Margaret snorted with derision and said, 'But she doesn't even bother wearing any make up. How can you say she's beautiful when I wear make up every day, and my tits are much better than hers?'

One of the nurses smiled kindly at Margaret and asked her how old she was.

'Forty-two,' Margaret responded.

I looked across at her and noticed the pudgy features. Drink had spoiled her once beautiful face and I did feel sorry for her. She had a good body; one she was proud enough to show off, but she looked her age and more.

The nurses looked from Margaret to me before one of them said: 'Yes, Margaret, you are only forty-two and Pauline has fourteen, nearly fifteen years on you, but despite coping with a very serious illness, she looks fantastic.'

Pouting her disapproval at the unfairness of it all, Margaret rounded on me with pure venom in her voice.

'If you'd had the life I've had to put up with,' she snarled at me, 'you wouldn't look that good. I bet you've never had an effing problem in your effing life. You don't even live in the real effing world, do you?'

She put her coat on, and took her mobile phone and cigarettes, and stormed off out of the bay, while the nurses continued giving out pills to the others.

If only she knew, I thought to myself, but it would have been a pointless exercise to tell her anything about myself. People like Margaret never listened to anyone else because they were so wrapped up in themselves. I kept quiet as I didn't want to inflame the situation any further. Although the nurses meant well, I couldn't help thinking that perhaps they fuelled the fire of discontent somewhat. It was better that I kept quiet, minded my own business and just kept myself to myself.

One night I had to get up and go to the toilet. I had to walk past the other beds to get to the main corridor and, as I went past the bed nearest the opening to the corridor, the woman (another alcoholic in her late sixties) suddenly started screaming. She was sitting up in bed as I tiptoed past, and she had been asleep, but on seeing me she began to scream. I went up to the nurses' station, told them about her, and then went to the bathroom. When I came out again, two nurses were trying to calm her down. As I made my way back to my own bed as quietly as possible, she screamed out:

'There she is! That bald-headed monster is the one who woke me up! She should be shot for creeping about the place and waking people up. She should be shot for being bald and scaring people who are trying to sleep.'

One of the nurses came over to me and helped me back into bed. I had started crying and the whole ward was awake now. I felt as if it was all my fault and I quietly sobbed onto this nurse's shoulder. 'Can't I go back into one of the single rooms?' I asked her.

'Sorry Pauline, there aren't any free at the moment.' She kept her arms around my shoulders trying to comfort me while the other nurse was battling to calm the other woman down.

Eventually she became quieter and, after one or two of the other patients had been to the bathroom, the ward settled down again. But that outburst had sealed my unpopularity and from then on, none of the women spoke to me at all.

The next day I felt pretty strange. Some of the nurses had had colds and I'd been coughing for a while now. I'd had a sore throat, but nothing had been done about either condition. But this particular day, while I was getting washed behind my drawn curtains, I felt very peculiar. I called out to one of the nurses as she was handling out pills to the women.

She came straight away and, just as she was opening the screens, I started to fall. She rushed over, caught me and helped me into bed. She opened the window slightly and took my temperature. It was up. My arms and legs felt like lead and I came close to passing out. She disappeared for a while, and then one of the doctors came to see me. They weren't sure what was wrong but later that afternoon I was transferred up to King's College Hospital.

As I left the ward in a wheelchair, Margaret, the woman who'd been so unkind, called out after me. 'Thank eff for that. Good effing riddance, freak.'

The porter who was wheeling me out looked at me horrified. I had filled up with tears again and, although I felt so ill, I was glad to be getting away from that ward. The 'couple of days' had astonishingly become nineteen days, and I felt more ill now than when I went in originally.

I slept on and off on the journey in the ambulance to King's College Hospital and I wondered what fate would await me once I got there.

Chapter 17 – CMV, MRSA and the flu! Really?

I was settled into a different room to the one I'd been in the previous month. It was slightly smaller than the first one but had everything I needed. Mel, one of the nurses who'd nursed me when I had my stem cell transplant, came to see me. He was shocked at how unwell I seemed.

Then, he heard me coughing and a nasal swab was arranged. I thought a nasal swab would just be like a cotton bud (Q tip) inserted in my nose and that would be that. Unfortunately, it was a bit more detailed (and uncomfortable) than that.

A thin tube with a little rubber cap was inserted in my nostril and pushed up as far as it would go. As this goes against the natural way the nostril would operate, it was very uncomfortable and made my eyes water. It ended up just above my eyebrow and it was the most unpleasant sensation I'd ever experienced – apart from the bone marrow tests which were horrific. Then the tube was brought back out of my nose and the contents sent to the laboratory for analysis.

Mel came back to me the following day, wearing a mask and plastic apron. He told me that I had the flu and would need to take Tamiflu for a few weeks. I was still having transfusions of Ganciclovir a couple of times a day, and now I needed to have Tamiflu tablets as well. One of the other nurses had swabbed me for MRSA, and I'd been found positive, so I had to wash and shower using a type of disinfectant soap. I couldn't believe it. Prior to going into Queen Mary's Hospital on Thursday, 8th March, I'd had 4 weeks at home after the stem cell transplant and I thought I was getting better. Now here I was, having been transferred up to King's with not only CMV, but MRSA and the flu also. How much worse could it get, I asked myself.

Now, anyone who entered my room had to wear a mask, from Abraham, the cleaner, to the people who brought meals and drinks and, of course, the doctors and nurses. It felt like I was a plague victim, and everyone had to be careful that they didn't catch it, or horror of horrors, that it somehow spread throughout the unit to everyone else. That was the benefit of being in a little room by myself – as were all the patients in the Derek Mitchell Unit; everyone was self-contained to minimise the risk of infection and cross infection.

No one told me about the side effects of Tamiflu. Almost immediately I was in need of the Pampers' type nappies again as I experienced fast and furious diarrhoea. When I was not actively having diarrhoea, I had seepage all the time. I can remember at this point, when I was still relatively aware of what was going on around me, of praying to God and telling him, quite indignantly, that I didn't sign up for seepage and that I'd be happy if he could see to it, as quickly as possible, that all explosions from my rear end were curtailed and we'd say no more about the matter. But I think he must have been busy that day, and every day thereafter, because both seepage and explosions continued ad nauseum.

I now plummeted into a very dark place indeed. My dreams were full of ghoulish objects, and I felt as if I was falling through blackness. Sometimes I would be free falling, arms flailing out to the sides, almost like a bird trying to fly. Other times I'd be hurtling through space locked in a tall cage, a bit like a lift but with bars all the way round. I could see out, but I was trapped as I sped through time and space, tumbling through the blackness with nothing else around me. My life and all that I knew was out of control and the darkness nightly took me on insane journeys to unknown destinations.

Had I slipped unnoticed from this world and this was now my fate? Was I destined for all time to spend my life – or was it my death? – just tumbling through the darkness locked forever in my cage? Was I in Hell?

I thought there was a Day of Judgement where all my sins would be laid out before me. But wasn't I forgiven anyway? Did Jesus not die for me on the Cross that I might know eternal life after all? Was I the only one who had not been excused because I hadn't had a note from my parents to explain why I was a sinner?

So, I'd missed out on going to Heaven by some biased jury and my punishment was to spend eternity locked in this cage, rolling, tumbling, hurtling through space? What had I done that was so bad that this was my penance?

It's been said that life on earth is actually Hell and that, in dying, we are released from Hell and ascend to Heaven. Certainly, my life had had its unfair share of dramas and traumas, but these had been – or so I thought when I reflected back on it from time to time – outweighed by times of unparalleled beauty and amazement. Giving birth to my two sons, Paul and David, was 'up there' as my two best achievements ever, having various articles published over the years counted as another high; meeting virtually every single pop star and group who were in the hit parade from the mid-sixties, when I worked at

IPC magazines when I was eighteen years of age, was worthy of a mention too. But somewhere, I must have done something terrible to warrant this living hell I now found myself in.

I'd been told that, as a child, I fought with my two brothers Kenny and Tony. Did that make me a bad person? They used to gang up on me and I'd retaliate. Their crimes against me went unnoticed. It was my acts of self-defence that were seen, noted, and stored for future examination and mention when my faults were regularly listed.

I do remember playing in a local park with Ken, Tony and some neighbourhood children of a similar age to us when we were quite young. We were daring each other to do silly things and although I hadn't been dared to do this, I pushed Kenny into the pond. I didn't know if he could swim but we fished him out immediately, and in our childish manner, laughed until our sides ached as he emerged from the pond covered in leaves and other debris that had been thrown in it.

Was this the heinous crime I had committed that relegated me to this Hell? Was I stuck? Could no one hear my cries for help, for forgiveness? Was I lost between worlds?

Being dead wasn't all it was cracked up to be, I thought in more lucid moments. Small. Insignificant. Unloved. With eyes open I blinked at the inky blackness. Or were my eyes closed and the inky blackness now lived behind my eyes? I was spiralling out of control into nothingness, a black void, and no one noticed that I was getting lost, falling through the cracks.

These dreams frightened me because I thought I was going mad, that my mind was being overcome with some dark forces that I couldn't control. I tried to tell one of the nurses, but I'm sure she thought I was hallucinating, or perhaps she did think that I was going insane. She just gave me a weak smile and a feeble look and zoomed back out of the room as quickly as she'd entered.

During my more coherent moments I was able to rationalise these dreams. I prayed every day that God would bring me through these trying times, and I asked him to surround me with angels to guard me and take care of me. So, couldn't the cages be thought of as metallic angels? That I was being protected from danger when I was in the cage, and that despite what I was going through, God was, in fact, protecting me? I wanted to believe that, at any rate. I couldn't believe that I was now so ill and having come through the rigours of chemotherapy, and the awful side effects of the stem cell transplant, that I was about to leave this world because of the flu.

Days ran like rivers into one another, and nights seemed one long continuation of darkness and anxious thoughts. I didn't have any energy; I couldn't fight any more and I knew I was beginning to give up. I couldn't get out of bed and I barely ate anything. It was, quite simply, the worst I had ever felt in my entire life and I was quite peeved to think I was going to die here alone in an unmade bed, with a soiled giant Pampers' nappy underneath me. The thought of death upset me as I thought of all the things I had wanted to accomplish in my life. I wanted to see my grandchildren grow up; I wanted to have my books published, and I hadn't quite given up on finding love – the thought that I might never be swept off my feet and experience the fullness and joy of being in love and in being loved – all saddened me. And yet, death seemed a such welcome friend in the dark hours of the night.

I didn't know that hallucinations and confusion were some

of the side effects of taking Tamiflu and that my dreams at night spilled into waking nightmares during the day. I was in hell and no one seemed to care – or that's how it seemed to me.

Astonishingly, one day, one of the consultants stood next to my bed and told me the incredible news that I was now better. He took his mask off and I saw his smile, which lit up his kind brown eyes.

'We nearly lost you,' he said. 'We've lost people with fewer health issues than you. You must have someone on your side.'

I smiled back at him, weakly. Had I really come through this seemingly unending nightmare? It didn't seem possible.

'Give it a couple more days and we'll see if you can't go home, Pauline,' he said, still smiling.

'Home,' I whispered, hardly daring to believe it. 'You mean … I can really go home?' I was almost in tears.

He put his hand on my shoulder and gently patted it. 'You're amazing, Pauline, you really are. Now just rest and think about going home. You need to get a bit stronger, but I think by the weekend you can probably go home.'

He went out of the room. If I could have done a jig to celebrate this unexpected news, I would have done so. But I had zero energy and I still couldn't get out of bed without a great deal of effort on my part and, besides, I was still attached to a giant fetid Pampers nappy.

Finally, on Wednesday 18 April five and a half weeks after being transferred to Kings, I was allowed to go home. I had spent a total of seven and a half weeks in hospital and lost over two and a half stone in weight. So much for being in hospital for 'just a few days' as I'd originally been told.

I called Ian, a friend of mine, who is a cab driver and he

came to pick me up. I was sick twice on the journey home, but I couldn't wait to get back to see if Timmy was all right, and whether or not he'd recognise me after being on his own for all that length of time. As I could hardly walk because I was so weak, Ian helped me to my front door and put my bags in the hallway for me. Then I almost crawled to the couch and waited for Timmy to come in from the garden.

I didn't have to wait long. When he came in the front room and saw me lying on the sofa, his little face lit up in recognition and pleasure. Mum was home; all was well in his little world again. He almost flew over to me and rubbed his head all around my face, mewing with delight. Then making a nest on the duvet next to me, he settled down alongside me for a happy rest.

I stroked his head and the silky fur on his back, overjoyed that I was home again and hoped there would be nothing on the horizon that would take me into hospital again. I was rewarded by the loudest purrs imaginable.

Ten days later I had to go back to Queen Mary's Hospital for another Linogram and the Hickman Line was removed. As before, the predicted twenty minutes turned into an ordeal lasting nearly two hours to remove it. Dr R performed the task as best he could, while a junior doctor looked on for experience.

He offered to hold my hand as I was finding it difficult to cope with the pain, despite copious amounts of lignocaine, a decision he probably regretted. My grip on his hand tightened and he began to squirm with the discomfort of being held in a vice. Finally, it was all over. Four stitches, as before, a battered and bruised breast, and a jagged incision. I hoped this was the last time I'd need to have a Hickman Line removed.

Chapter 18 – Signs of progress

At the end of May, about six weeks after I came out of the hospital, Janice, my friend with the cattery, brought Ricky home. It took a little while for him to acknowledge me, but he gave me a lovely head rub, purring madly. He had a sore ear, which Kevin, our vet, operated on a few days later.

I had to have another bone marrow test at King's College Hospital on the day of Ricky's operation, so Janice kindly collected him from my house and took him to the vets'. She kept him back at her cattery until his stitches were removed, which was about three weeks later.

On Sunday 2 June Janice brought Sam home. Timmy, having spent all these months on his own with me, was not pleased to see Sam and they had a few spats. After a couple of days, they settled down and both shared sofa duties looking after me.

Two weeks later, Billy and Ollie came home, leaving poor Ricky at the cattery by himself. Both cats were really happy to see me, and later on in the day, Billy resumed his position of sitting on the sofa behind my head and patting it with his paws. I had a wispy look going on with my hair but that didn't deter Billy from licking it. He also made a point of sitting on my lap while I did my knitting, wanting cuddles. So, it was a case of 'Knit one, stroke one' – while I watched television!

Within a few days, the four cats had settled back into their old routines; apart from Timmy, the other three had been in the cattery for four months. My routine didn't vary that much: from blood tests twice a week at one hospital; monthly appointments at both hospitals; and assorted appointments for lung function tests and liver tests. I was out of the house virtually every single day of the week – at one hospital or another, but it was always good to come home to my welcome committee of three ginger cats and one sleek black one who thought he was a ginger.

Ricky came home later in June. His ear had healed but he wasn't eating. He seemed down in the dumps and although the other cats were pleased to see him, nothing would entice him to eat. I tried everything, from hand feeding him bits of chicken, to slightly warming his food in the microwave. He wasn't interested.

He had never been a lap cat, although he would sit as close to my thigh as he possibly could. I'd cuddle him, and tell him how beautiful he was, and he'd purr like a tractor. But still he wouldn't eat.

I did wonder if being in the cattery for nearly five months had brought back memories of when he'd been kept in a rabbit hutch for a year by the people who had him before he was rescued by the RSPCA. Maybe he thought I'd abandoned him, especially once the other three had come home and he was there by himself recovering from the operation on his ear.

I took him back to see Kevin, our vet, twice the following week. He had blood tests, urine tests, stool tests, all revealing nothing out of the ordinary. I tried everything in my power to get Ricky to eat. I knew he was hungry because he always went to his food bowl when I put it down, then he'd walk away. If I hand fed him bits of tuna in brine or chicken, he'd eat a mouthful before walking away.

On Tuesday 24 July Ricky went back to the vets for an exploratory exam of his nose. He hadn't eaten anything for nearly four weeks, and he'd lost a considerable amount of weight. He was kept at the vets for observation and four days later, on the Friday, Kevin rang me with devastating news. Ricky had lymphoma of the nasal passages. Chemotherapy wasn't an option because of my precarious state of health, so my precious fluffy ginger boy had to be put to sleep. He had only been back home with me for barely four weeks.

I raced up to the surgery and they put me in a special room out the back, so that I would be protected from any germs that might have been lurking in the waiting-room. They brought Ricky in and left us to have some quality time together. I told him how special he was and how much joy he had brought to me, and the other cats. I told him that I loved him with all my heart. He gave me a couple of gentle head butts which was his way of showing affection. We spent about thirty minutes together before Kevin came in to release Ricky from his discomfort.

My heart was broken again, just over a year after losing Garfield.

The months wore on. Timmy, Sam, Billy and Ollie were pleased to be back home, and I was glad to have them home. I was getting stronger day by day and I could see progress in my body.

Wednesday 5 December 2007, I had my first proper bath since May. It was wonderful to be able to lie down in the bath and relax. From May, I had to use a special bath seat as I had difficulty getting in and out of the bath. My very long stay in hospital in March and April had left me weak and unsteady. My bath has very deep sides and I couldn't lift my legs over the sides or pull myself out again afterwards.

Although the bath seat was a very useful item to have, bath time was never as relaxing as it used to be. I'd get into the bath, stand up and soap myself all over and then sit down on the seat. I'd press the button on the control panel and the bath seat would lower me into the water, where I'd rinse the soap off me. Then I'd press another control to bring me back up again to a level where I could stand up and start drying myself before getting out of the bath.

I always felt rather regal when the seat was in the process of raising me up again. If Timmy was hovering near the bath-room door – on duty – I'd give him a royal wave as if I was acknowledging his faithful companionship.

So, to finally be able to have a bath without help was a sure sign of progress for me. The bath seat had been removed on Monday 3 December and I'd been nervous about taking a bath without it, so I'd spent those couple of days just getting myself psyched up. Silly, wasn't it? But once I got in the bath, it was pure heaven! And while in the bath, I gave thanks, as always, to God for bringing me this far!

About a week or so before Christmas, I had the last of my evening meals the ladies from my church cooked for me. Gradually, since August, the meals were being petered out giving me the chance to start cooking and fending for myself. At first, I didn't cook anything elaborate. I had forgotten completely how to cook anyway, and I think my first meal was a jacket potato with cheese. Not much can go wrong there. Some of my other meals were less successful and co-ordination was a bit hit and miss. Either the meat was cooked but the vegetables weren't, or more usually, the vegetables were ready, but the meat was still grinning defiantly in pink juices.

The ladies of my church had been wonderful. Since coming out of hospital in February after the transplant, my friend Brenda, who was a Pastoral Assistant in our church, had liaised with them and they had provided evening meals every day for months on end. I will never forget their kindness. I know I must have seemed a bit picky at times. Chemotherapy alters the taste buds and certain foods made me sick just to look at them, let alone smell them. And I was sick for months and months after eating. It didn't seem to matter what I ate, or what time, even my breakfast cereal wasn't exempt from a rapid journey into the bucket or toilet – whichever was closer!

I started off having about half a palm-sized portion because I just couldn't eat very much. As the weeks became months, so the portion sizes grew little by little until I was eating an almost normal serving for a person of my size.

The ladies knew I couldn't eat certain foods, so they did the best with what I could eat; and there were some occasions when I might be served the same meal – albeit cooked slightly differently – several times in the same week. I recall one memorable week when I had minced beef four times. It had been dished up as a shepherd's pie, spaghetti Bolognese and plain mince with vegetables. But I don't actually like mince and although I ate it, I was sick after each dinner. In the end, I had to ask Brenda to tactfully ask the ladies not to give me mince! I did feel slightly ungrateful, but I can't stand the texture or taste of mince and I haven't eaten it since.

Around mid to late June, I stopped having the carer. The

client she saw before she came to me was going into respite care for a month. My slot would now be 6.30 instead of 7.30 in the morning. I didn't want to get up at that time just to have a wash and eat my breakfast. We agreed to stop but if I ever needed a carer again, Kim would be more than happy to return. She hoped I wouldn't need her services and wished me luck.

On December 24 I had my fourth haircut since my hair began growing back. After nearly six months of being bald my hair grew back and, although it looked similar to how it looked before, it was noticeably different in texture and feel. It grew back in several shades of grey, so I jokingly say that my hair colour is now tabby-cat grey.

Knowing what I know about chemical hair dyes, I intended to leave it grey, but I waited a number of months, before having highlights put in, which completely transformed both the look of my hair and my face. I was very pleased with how it turned out. I won't have it done too often; now and then will be all right just to keep me feeling good about myself.

But it's the texture that has surprised me. It's so much softer than it ever used to be. My hair comes from my father's side of the family: thick, curly and coarse. You would never run your fingers through it because it was so coarse that you'd have your skin peeled off for you! It was like a Brillo pad – those scourers used to clean burnt saucepans - and growing up with it was a nightmare, as I never knew how to dress it properly. My Mum used to get it cut at the beginning of the school term, and it would just grow and grow until the beginning of the next term, when it would be almost shaved again.

I had been told by the nurses and doctors that when hair grows back after chemotherapy it's much thicker and curlier.

I had groaned at the time as it was already thick and curly – and now it would be more so. I joked with the nurses that if it became any thicker or curlier, I'd have pigeons nesting in it.

It's so soft now that I find myself constantly touching it – something I never did before. My hairdresser friend, Lesley, who cuts it regularly for me, has mentioned on a couple of occasions how soft it is and it's much straighter now – which is a bit of a surprise.

A year after going into Queen Mary's with the virus in my blood and ending up in King's fighting for my life with the flu and MRSA, March 12 2008, was a breakthrough day for me – a milestone, in fact. I saw Dr W in clinic, and she said that I could now go for the blood tests fortnightly instead of weekly. This was music to my ears. I was getting my life back! After months and months of having blood tests twice a week, then just once a week, and now, I was able to go every two weeks instead.

I half expected the hospital transport to turn up as usual on the following Monday despite changing the 'standing order' but, fortunately, they didn't. My next-door neighbour, Marge, and I went to our local shopping centre to get our usual weekly shop. The whole week felt very strange as if I was missing something and was out of sync with the days.

I was used to being up early every Monday, so that I was ready for when either an ambulance crew or a car picked me up. Then, I'd walk down the long corridor to the chemotherapy unit where I'd collect my blood forms, and then wait in the pathology department to be called. Sometimes I'd get a coffee and read the paper or chat to other people, while I waited for transport to take me home again.

It was all I'd known for so long that it felt weird to do something else instead of going to the hospital.

But I saw this for what it was: a sign of progress and *that* could only be a good sign. In addition to having my blood tests done on a fortnightly basis, I had, for a couple of months, been having my clinic appointments with Dr W, on a six-weekly basis – which had been the first sign of progress. King's College Hospital still saw me in their outpatient clinic on a monthly basis but, slowly and surely, I felt as if my life was getting back on track.

Chapter 19 – January 2008 – Revelations and resolutions

Life is like a river, constantly moving. It may trickle in some places or it may rush along gathering momentum as it flows, finding new paths or outlets for its constant energy. A river – or water in general – is an analogy for Life. How many of us have stagnated in a pond of algae, too fearful to move or change direction or course? The little we know gives us a modicum of comfort, but we are too nervous to step out and embrace change.

I had become afraid. I was too scared to live in case I died! I was fearful of going out to places like church or the shopping mall where there would be many people, in case I caught something from someone which could put me back in hospital. Having almost died in April 2007 with the flu, I was terrified that I might catch something else that could finish me off. So, I stayed indoors, only venturing forth when I had to go to hospital or to the local Post Office to send prizes off to the subscribers who entered the monthly Book Quiz in the Mewsletter, or general letters to friends.

I was challenged one day in early January 2008 when I met up with Therese, one of my 'Waiting-room' friends in the Pathology department of Queen Mary's Hospital where we were both having our weekly blood tests.

Therese had a different kind of leukaemia and had previously, on diagnosis, been given a two-month prognosis. This was some months prior to us becoming acquainted. She'd had a stem cell transplant and, within a few days, of being back at home she was out and about walking up to five miles a day.

I was speechless when she told me. I couldn't even walk as far as the bus stop – or I assumed I couldn't, but I hadn't actually tried. She asked me how I did my shopping.

'Online,' I replied.

'And how do you buy your clothes?' she asked me.

'From catalogues or online,' I answered her, feeling edgy.

Her eyebrows shot up in disbelief. 'Don't you go out of the house at all?' she asked.

'Er, well, no. No, not really,' I replied feeling more uncomfortable. 'I'm scared I'll catch something. Having caught the flu last year and nearly dying, I'm terrified I'm going to catch something which might nearly kill me again – and perhaps succeeding this time!' I added, giving weight to my argument for living the life of a hermit.

'You'll never build up your immune system against these things if you stay indoors all the time,' Therese said, kindly. 'Before I was diagnosed, I used to walk between ten and fifteen miles a day. Now, I'm walking five to ten miles each day. It's surprising how good it makes me feel. I'd go mad if I was cooped up indoors all day, every day.'

'Well,' I began, 'I've got my cats, my computer, my website, my writing projects, my books …. I've got enough to keep me mentally stimulated and busy.'

'That's all very well,' Therese exclaimed, 'you're busy, but you're by yourself and you're not getting any fresh air or exercise. You need both – they will help you to sleep better. If you can get a good night's sleep, you'll feel so much better the following day. You'll be mentally alert and not sluggish.'

I'd explained to Therese previously that I had trouble getting to bed before midnight each night and, as a result I always had to have a sleep right after breakfast. I'd get up between 7 – 8 am on non-hospital days, feed the cats, have breakfast and then I'd lie on the sofa and sleep for another hour or so. Only then, did I feel I could face the world and whatever the day would bring.

The downside of all this inactivity was that I wasn't tired enough to go to bed earlier, so the scenario would repeat itself each day. I felt as if I was out of control; always tired but not tired enough to go to sleep at night. Therese's words were making sense to me.

As if my chance encounter with Therese wasn't enough, there had been an elderly lady that we'd picked up on our way to hospital that morning in the patients' ambulance. She was riddled with rheumatoid arthritis, bless her, and had had a fall a few months previously. She'd broken her hip in three places, but she'd been sent home from hospital untreated because it hadn't shown up on the x-rays that had been taken.

After three days of intense agonising pain, she had been finally admitted to hospital where she'd stayed for three weeks, the doctor finally realising that that she'd broken her hip.

Although her body was twisted and bent with the ravages of rheumatoid arthritis, her mind was as sharp as a knife, and she was a delight to talk to on the journey to the hospital. She said some quite thought-provoking things which made me sit up and take notice.

'You've got to keep going, love,' she said, smiling. 'I'm blessed. I'm luckier than some, so you have to keep going.'

Blinking back tears, I smiled at her and agreed.

The journey back home in the ambulance was also 'meant' as there was another elderly lady who'd been to a clinic. She, too, had had a fall indoors and had been sent to have physiotherapy. She struck up a conversation with me and, almost uncannily, continued the theme of the first lady's conversation and Therese's conversation as well. Were these angels with messages for me?

'I won't let that chair get me,' she said forcefully. 'If you sit down all day long and do nothing, you get weaker and weaker, until you really can't do anything – so, then, you have to sit down all day long,' she said. 'I keep saying, all the time I can do things, I will do them. I don't let anyone help me all the while I am capable of doing things for myself. That chair isn't going to claim me!' she said again.

I thought of my slothful existence and felt very guilty. There was Therese with a more serious form of leukaemia than I'd got, walking miles every day. There were those two elderly ladies with far worse health issues than I had, being independent and getting about – not quite unaided – but to the best of their ability. And there was me – too afraid to go out and find my way in the world in case I caught something from someone and died.

I'd forgotten how to live, and I was determined that I was going to make some changes.

Chapter 20 – Setbacks and disappointments

Since having the stem cell transplant the previous January, from about April onwards, I'd had persistently abnormal liver function test results. I was referred to Dr Heneghan, the liver consultant at King's College Hospital, on 7 November. He examined me, and more blood tests were done, the result of which, the following Wednesday, I had to go into hospital for a liver biopsy.

The biopsy was carried out the following day. I wasn't allowed any breakfast and, as I was taking pain killers for the pains I was experiencing, I was very sick. I didn't know that taking pain killers on an empty stomach made you sick. The biopsy was not particularly pleasant, and I was awake throughout. I was aware of a pulling sensation, which was a bit uncomfortable.

I returned to my room on the ward and had to spend the rest of the day lying on my side. This was so that I didn't bleed to death! The following day, I was allowed home. Ian, the cab driver, who usually took me to and from King's College Hospital, collected me and as usual, I was sick several times on the journey home. Ian was always very kind and patient with me, stopping the car whenever he could to allow me the dignity of throwing up by the kerb.

I had earmarked January 2008 as my benchmark month. I saw it as my month for new beginnings, for getting back into the swing of things and trying to get back into a normal way of life again. After 18 months of weekly hospital visits, chemotherapy, the stem cell transplant, the 'blip' in March 2007 where a few days in hospital became a nightmarish fight for life for seven and a half weeks, I was ready for some semblance of normality to resume. To be honest, I was bored with living almost like a recluse – I wanted to be part of the 'action' again.

In December, I told myself that when January arrived, I would return to doing some of my 'old' things. I went to church on Christmas Day morning and after the service, I went up to the Worship Team where they hugged me and held me like a precious find. I used to sing with them on Sunday mornings, and now I asked if I could maybe try out with them again on the next rehearsal date – a few days later. My one problem was the residual cough that I'd had as a legacy of the flu I caught in March the previous year. I didn't know if I could sing without coughing, but the only way we'd find out was to give it a try.

Thursday arrived and I was so excited. When we work through the songs we're going to sing in Sunday's service, we always have our own special time with the Lord and many of the songs we've sung have brought us into the presence of the Holy Spirit. We've felt a wonderful connection which I dubbed 'having a special moment'. We all looked forward to having a special moment during our rehearsal times.

Although I did cough a fair bit, I managed to sing the songs and, even though I was terribly nervous about how my voice sounded usually, no one said it sounded bad. So, I was looking forward, as part of my 'getting back to normal routine,' to returning to church full time starting with the coming Sunday.

The following day, Friday, I had an upset stomach which lasted until early Sunday morning. I had to make the decision whether to go to church in case I either gave someone a bug, or I picked something else up which would make me worse and I'd end up in hospital. I was bitterly disappointed.

There were more disappointments to come.

When I saw Dr W at our monthly outpatient's appointment on 19 December, she said that the Epstein-Barr Virus (EBV) levels in my blood were very high. In fact, the levels were 92,000 (ninety-two thousand!) and the acceptable level is ten, which is a humongous difference. King's College Hospital wanted me to go the following Monday (Christmas Eve) to have some treatment. Knowing what travelling up to London by train is like at the best of times and, knowing how dreadful it would be on Christmas Eve, I said I didn't want to go. I already had an outpatient's appointment scheduled for the 2 January at King's, so I thought it would be alright to wait and we would discuss it then.

On the day of my appointment, in discussion with the consultant at King's College Hospital, it was decided that I would go up to the Haematology Unit the following Tuesday and for the next three Tuesdays after that, to have an intra-venous transfusion of RITUXIMAB (which always looks like it is an anagram to me!) As there are side effects to any drug, I asked my friend Brenda to come with me in case I was taken sick on the train journey home.

Prior to the treatment beginning, when I'd arrived for my earlier outpatient's appointment, I had a lot of pain down the right side of my neck under my ear. I'd been having various really sharp pains in different parts of my upper body since November, when it was thought that shingles might be about to erupt. I was given a course of ACICLOVIR, but nothing happened – the shingles didn't come out. However, the pains persisted and spread all over my upper torso, being much worse in my head and neck. None of the medical staff at either hospital had any suggestions as to what the cause might be, and I did wonder if perhaps I was imagining it – but no, a pain like that had me in tears at times. I had been given pain killers to help alleviate the pain, but they didn't really work.

Dr Paul Westward, the consultant I saw at Kings, rang up Queen Mary's Hospital in Sidcup and asked if it were possible for me to see someone (from the Ear, Nose, and Throat department) as a matter of urgency. He explained to them that I was in severe pain and it could be a middle ear infection.

The next morning – still in pain – but exhausted from my journey and waiting around at the hospital for several hours – I was resting on the sofa when the phone rang. It was one of the medical secretaries at Queen Mary's who had managed to get me on the waiting list of that morning's clinic with Mr Harris, the top Ear, Nose, and Throat specialist at Queen Mary's. I panicked. I wasn't washed or dressed – and I needed hospital transport to get me to the hospital as I still wasn't allowed to use public transport.

A car duly arrived for me at around 10.00am, and I checked in to the clinic at around 10.45. I was told there was a very full clinic with a long waiting time, so it could be several hours before I'd be seen. Taking a book with me is par for the course on all my hospital appointments, and so I smiled. I was still in a lot of pain, but the fact that Mr Harris was going to see me made life a lot more bearable, as he is a wonderfully kind and patient man.

I sat down, got my glasses out of their case, put them on,

and got my book out of the bag. At that moment, my name was called! So much for waiting several hours!

Mr Harris was very thorough in his examination of my ears, head and neck. He sprayed a nasal anaesthetic up my nose so that he could insert a narrow tube up it to see what was going on. Apparently, nothing was going on. There were no sinus problems, no signs of infection caused by mucus or anything, and he was quite happy with me.

As some of the anaesthetic had gone down my throat, my throat was now 'frozen' and felt weird! Especially when I tried to swallow! It felt like a huge stone was trying to drop down my throat.

I felt relieved that there didn't seem to be a medical reason for the pains, but it didn't take away from the fact that I still had them, and I was in agony. I did have pain killers which I was eating like Smarties but the downside of taking pain killers is that they can cause constipation – so I now had a different kind of pain.

At 9.00am on Tuesday the 9 January, a cab called for me along with my friend Brenda. The cab then took us down to the station where we caught the train to Denmark Hill. From there, it was a short walk to King's College Hospital. The treatment finally began in the afternoon, despite the fact we had arrived in the department by just after 10.15, and it took over four hours to go through the drip. The nurse who had removed the canula, hadn't checked the wound afterwards. As I was putting my coat on, I was alarmed to see blood dripping on the floor. I wrenched my coat off to find blood all over my jumper and it continued to pump out. The nurse sprang into action, mopping me up, putting a dressing on the wound, and making sure I had stopped bleeding before they let us leave the department.

We finally got back to our respective homes around 7.00pm. I'm sure Brenda was very tired, but I was totally zonked out. As I didn't 'suffer' any side effects, I told Brenda that she needn't come with me for the following three weeks. It had been pretty boring for me and I had slept part the way through the treatment, but it must have been even more tedious for Brenda, despite having a book with her. As there is always something going on in the department, it's hard to concentrate on reading, no matter how brilliant the book is!

And so that was the pattern for January. Every Monday I'd go to Queen Mary's for my weekly blood tests and every Tuesday I caught the train to Denmark Hill for the weekly RITUXIMAB transfusion. On two different Wednesdays I had to attend outpatient's appointments, both at King's College Hospital and at Queen Mary's, and on the last week of the month, I had to go back again on the Thursday to have a lymphocyte transfusion as well. It was a purely dreadful month – with three hospital visits every week. I was absolutely exhausted.

I was also attending a creative writing class on Friday mornings, which I'd joined late in the term in November, in my bid to get back to some normality. I was just getting into my stride when the next problem hit.

Chapter 21 – Shingles and shopping

February dawned, and I woke up one Saturday morning to a few funny looking red marks at the top of my left bum cheek. By Sunday morning, these had spread around and above the hip to the line of my stomach, and below my 'apron'. They were angry red welts and at first, I thought they were an allergic reaction to the ALLOPURINOL I'd had to take in conjunction with having the RITUXIMAB.

I decided not to go to church just in case I was hatching something which could be caught by others and, on the Monday, when I went up to the Chemotherapy Unit at Queen Mary's Hospital to pick up my blood forms, I showed them to Yvonne, the chemo nurse. By now, there were even more of the little beggars, and my entire left side was just a mass of angry red blisters.

'Oh, you've got shingles,' Yvonne said. 'I'll get Dr R to confirm it and we'll see what you'll have to do.'

Although there wasn't anyone else in the waiting-room, she put me into one of the side rooms used for treatment to keep me out of anyone's way, and I waited for Dr R to appear. He came soon enough, and I showed him the red welts. He agreed I had shingles and wanted me to stay in hospital, that very day for a seven days' course of ACICLOVIR given intravenously.

I wasn't happy about that. In light of what happened to me the previous March, when what started out as supposedly being a few days in hospital had turned into a marathon seven-and-a-half-weeks fight for life. I bartered with him. In the end, he said he would speak to the pharmacist to see what he could advise. I begged. I pleaded. 'I don't want to come into hospital' I cried.

He came back to me – smiling. It would seem that fortune was on my side, and I could stay at home and take the ACICLOVIR five times a day, orally. But there were provisos. I had to promise that if anything (out of a long list that Dr R spelt out to me) occurred, I had to get myself to the hospital IMMEDIATELY. I promised!

The shingles lasted a couple of weeks, but the pain was intense and much worse than the strange, unexplained pains I'd experienced back in November. It was thought then that I might be getting shingles, but nothing had happened. It was a relief when the blisters finally dried up and disappeared.

When I came out of hospital back in February 2007, after the transplant, four of the cats were in the cattery and I just had Timmy at home with me. As the ladies from church were cooking my evening meals, I didn't need very much in the way of shopping. But as the cats came back home one by one from June onwards, I started to do my shopping online because I still wasn't going out anywhere, other than to the hospital, and more recently, to my creative writing class.

My neighbour, Marge, and I used to go shopping every Monday prior to the leukaemia being diagnosed, and one Sunday afternoon I telephoned her and asked if she'd like to come shopping with me the following day. I initially said I didn't feel up to trawling round all the shops we used to go into, before ending up at the store where we bought our main weekly shopping. She agreed to go with me, and I excitedly made a list of all the things I thought I needed. I still wasn't really back into the swing of things, and it took a few weeks to work out that I needed to keep an eye on things which might be running low, so that I wouldn't be completely out of whatever it was.

But on this first shopping trip, I was up early and couldn't contain my excitement. I knocked on Marge's front door at 10.30 and, like a child, I can remember saying to her: 'Marge! We're going shopping!' She laughed at me, probably thinking I was mad. But it wasn't until we were actually in Bexleyheath – which is our shopping centre –when I remembered that I don't really enjoy shopping!

I usually only go shopping once a week to get all the necessary provisions for the cats and myself for the entire week. Unless it's urgent, if I run out of something, I waited until the following week to buy it; only occasionally would I go out mid-week or towards the weekend to buy something I might need, because I really genuinely hated having to go shopping.

It was the initial excitement of being out of the house, and doing something different, which was so invigorating. For almost a year, the only time I left home was to go to hospital, either Queen Mary's or Kings. The previous November, I'd begun a creative writing class which I enjoyed, but here I was, actually doing something towards my daily life, and providing for me and the cats.

I was euphoric and felt sure that Therese would have been very pleased with me for making an effort. And it was a big effort, because I'd become so used to staying indoors, other than the hospital appointments, that I was nervous of being out 'in the big wide world.'

I remember that we went to Asda, the main supermarket that

we used, and bought the things on my list, Marge buying what she needed. We can't possibly carry home all our shopping, so we always get a cab and split the fare between us. We arrived home and the cab driver took our respective bags to our front doors. It took me nearly an hour to unload my shopping. It wasn't because I'd bought such a lot of stuff. It was purely and simply because I was exhausted! I had to sit down every few minutes to have a rest, and once it was all put away, I lay on the sofa and slept for two hours with the cats clustered around me, purring their socks off.

Marge and I went shopping most weeks. We soon began adding lunch to our time out and tentative visits to other shops and, before long, it was almost like I'd never been away. I did notice lots of changes in the year since I'd been shopping. Bus fares had risen, some of the shops had closed down and, of course, food prices had gone up.

But, just the sheer joy of being 'normal' and doing 'normal' everyday things carried me along. I always gave thanks to God for blessing me in so many ways; just being able to shop with Marge was a blessing in itself. Although there had been some disappointments and setbacks, the blessings didn't stop flowing.

Chapter 22 – Easter 2008

I was hell-bent on getting myself an Easter egg, but the £10 Baileys Easter egg that had been on Asda's shelves for the past three or four weeks, was gone - they had no eggs at all, and now the urgency to consume chocolate was becoming a demonic rage within me. Using the guise of posting a letter at the post office (quite a longish walk after the marathon Monday morning shopping experience with Marge), I went out with one thought on my mind. I remembered a really funny sketch by the writer and comedian, Ben Elton. He was talking about the thousands of commuters that disgorge into the main London train stations, after their day's work, to catch their train home. No one wants to sit next to anyone else, so they have this mantra: 'Double seat, gotta get a double seat.'

I chanted my own version of the mantra as I walked: 'Easter Egg, Easter Egg, gotta get an Easter Egg!' My local newsagent was woefully inadequate, and recommended the open-all-hours off licence, which sells everything, about thirty yards up the road in the opposite direction to where I needed to go.

I decided to walk up to the post office to post the get-well card to a friend, who had just had an operation, and while there I glanced across the road to the large newsagents - closed. I walked up to Somerfield - a shop I hate because it always seems so filthy with the dire staff yelling across the store to each other: 'Wayne, got any cheddar cheese on the deli?' To which

Wayne yells back: 'Nah, ain't got none.' Another unsatisfied customer leaves.

I glanced quickly round the store, not wanting to stay too long in case I caught bad English off the staff and, sad to say, they didn't have a single Easter egg lurking.

My need was becoming an obsession. 'Easter Egg, Easter Egg, gotta get an Easter Egg!' I walked back down the road to the open-all-hours off licence which sells everything - except Easter eggs. More disappointment. Suddenly, I had a divine inspiration: The Spar shop at the garage. Surely, they'd have an egg - even a bashed in broken egg would do.

I walked across the road and down a few yards trying to close my nose to the smell of petrol fumes. I walked into the Spar shop and was greeted with an overwhelming choice of Easter Eggs - all at half price. I was in Chocolate Heaven. I picked up one beautiful specimen with four bars of chocolate in the packaging - £2.50 was the price I had to pay for this slice of gorgeousness.

I rushed home dribbling and salivating. Tearing off my gloves, scarf, beanie, coat, trainers and socks, I rushed into the front room where I peeled off the golden foil and spread it neatly on my lap to catch any slivers of chocolate which I could lick up afterwards! And then, the joyous taste of chocolate. It was bliss - it made my hike worth it. And I now had 4 bars of chocolate to enjoy some other time.

It's funny because I'm not a chocoholic; I don't buy chocolate very often. In fact, I rarely buy sweets at all, and since I found out that cancer feeds on sugar, I've given all sweet things, including sugar, a wide berth, but every now and then I get a craving for something. I always allow myself a little treat

- nothing major - just a little bar of something that I appreciate, simply because it is a treat and, boy, did I enjoy that Easter egg!

Chapter 23 – Lymphocytes and GVHD

The results of the latest chimerism test I'd had done in early October, were disappointing. A chimerism test is a blood test which shows the percentage or ratio of cells: my brother Tony's cells to mine. Only five percent of the cells were his, which meant that the other ninety-five percent were mine. Obviously, we had to get to a point where there would be 100% of Tony's cells in my body and none of my own left.

It was now ten months since the stem cell transplant in January, and the doctors were hoping that his cells would have taken over mine by now. I hadn't had any symptoms of Graft Versus Host Disease (GVHD) which would have shown up when my body (the Host) started to fight the 'foreign' bodies (the Graft).

There were two things we could try. One: I could have chemotherapy and start over again. Or two: I would be given lymphocyte infusions over a period and hope they would kick-start the stem cells into doing the job they were destined to do. I didn't want to have chemotherapy again. I couldn't face the unwanted side effects and how ill I felt all the time. Lymphocyte infusions would be painless, going through the Hickman Line and the only side effects would be – hopefully – Graft Versus Host Disease. Lymphocytes are white blood cells which were taken at the same time as the stem cells were harvested from Tony.

On Wednesday 26 March I had an appointment at the outpatients' clinic at King's College Hospital in Denmark Hill. I was also having the last of three lymphocyte infusions. I'd had the first one in November 2007, and the second on the 2 of January 2008. After a two-hour wait for my appointment to come round, during which time I read almost the whole of book one of Marilyn Edward's delightful books, 'The Coach House Cats', regaling her life with her beloved cats, I finally saw Jin, one of the SHO's.

She had discussed in detail the reason for having the lymphocyte infusions and the fact that, at four point two million cells, this last dose was ten times greater than the first transfusion, and four times greater than the second one, and that at this amount, the very real and likely risk of side–effects, namely Graft Versus Host Disease (GVHD), would be possible.

A wonderful picture came into my mind of someone counting all those cells; 'one, two, three, three million, nine hundred and ninety-nine thousand … darn, I've just lost count. One, two, three ….'

Jin then described in graphic detail the likely scenario with regard to the side – effects ranging from the mild, (a rash, broken flaky skin) to the extreme, (liver problems which would show up as jaundiced skin) and an all-over rash like a bad case of sunburn, shivering, diarrhoea, vomiting, etc. It didn't sound too good. But, in one sense, although I was worried about having any of these symptoms, there was also a need for me to get some form of GVHD – hopefully the milder form – because at least it would show that my brother's cells were not just lying there passively, that they were, at least, fighting their corner for supremacy. So, whilst I didn't want to 'suffer' more than necessary, I did realise the 'sense' in getting a little bit of GVHD.

The next lot of news was a lot harder to take. I asked Jin whether I would be 'cured' of the leukaemia and how long that might be likely to take. Would I ever revert back to the old Pauline, pre-leukaemia diagnosis?

I was not prepared for her answer. It seems that doctors don't like to use the word 'cured' when it comes to illnesses like leukaemia. They prefer to use words like being in 'remission', and with this type of leukaemia, one can be in remission for up to twenty years, there being an eighty percent chance of going into remission. I was originally happy with those odds because gaining another twenty years would take me to my mid-late seventies, and I would be very pleased with that.

But, as for whether I would ever get back the 'old' Pauline – the one prior to getting leukaemia – well, that was a different matter. It seems that the stem cell transplant I had been given was what is called a 'soft and gentle' approach to tackling the leukaemia. Apparently, if I had had the more aggressive treatment, a bone marrow transplant, at my age (then fifty-six) it would not have been viable, and I would have died. So, it was better to treat it gently in the hope that Tony's cells would do their job adequately, and I would remain in remission. BUT, and it's a big but, I would never be completely 100% well again; there would always be the risk that the leukaemia could come back – and this is despite the eighty percent chance of remaining in remission.

This was not the news I wanted to hear. To put it mildly, I was devastated. I decided not to tell anyone in my close family circle or friends, in view of what happened when I told them originally about the leukaemia diagnosis. I couldn't bear to go through all that negativity again, and I didn't want to upset anyone else. I would keep this news to myself for the time being, work on it for a while and see what I could do to deal with it effectively. Then, and only then, would I test the water and see what reactions might be. If there was the faintest whiff of histrionics, then I would keep the news to myself and not divulge it at all.

Knowing how difficult it was for people to accept the news when I was first diagnosed with leukaemia, I knew that it would most likely be near to impossible for this latest piece of news to be viewed dispassionately, and for me to be treated with compassion or sympathy. I didn't want the phone put down on me again. I didn't want fragile conversations where I always seemed to be on the losing end of the argument because the person doing the arguing felt I was being the 'centre of atten-tion' and somehow, my having leukaemia made life difficult for them. I truly did not want to face such aggression and antagonism again.

I hoped my faith would pull me through this latest setback as I saw it. Perhaps this was the time God would conduct his greatest miracle! I had always wondered why – despite the zillions of prayers that had been uttered for me – I hadn't been healed. Being a natural coward, I hadn't wanted to go into hospital for several weeks having the course of aggressive, intensive chemotherapy. It wasn't because I would go bald – losing my hair was the least of my worries. It was because of all the dreadful side–effects that chemotherapy causes. Who in their right mind wouldn't want to pass up the opportunity of not having chemo? So, I had desperately wanted God to heal me BEFORE I got to that stage.

But – all the best laid plans etc. didn't come to pass and have the chemotherapy I did, losing my hair, my dignity but not quite my eyebrows. I then began to think a different way. If God wasn't going to heal me (yet) then there must be a very good reason why I was going to have to go through the rigours of chemotherapy. Perhaps I needed to learn some lessons. Perhaps someone else needed to see how I coped with chemotherapy and would make a commitment to God based on my positive attitude and faith? There were lots of 'perhaps' going on in my mind, and as none of us can ever know the mind of God, I obviously didn't have an answer.

The friends I met in the 'Waiting-room' were all going through different stages of their illnesses; some of them had various cancers and some had various types of leukaemia; many of us had had courses of chemotherapy followed by a stem cell transplant. If I had been healed before having my course of chemotherapy, I never would have met them in my ordinary journey of life because our paths never would have crossed. Was I meant to meet these wonderfully stoic folk? Perhaps they were meant to be part of my journey, to buoy me up in ways that my family members and close friends were unable to do. Perhaps I was meant to be part of their journey, that they would see something in me with which to hold on to, that my faith would hopefully strengthen them in some way.

I didn't have any answers. I only knew that God had walked with me throughout the entire journey and, far from my faith faltering when I was obviously not healed, it was strengthened by the knowledge that so many people around the world were praying for me and my complete recovery. God is a God who cares. He is a God who understands what his children are going through. And he hates for us to be sick and to suffer. He is a God who answers prayers and he is a God who performs miracles today just as he did in Biblical days. And I believed passionately, with all my heart, that my 'suffering' was not to be in vain; that someone somewhere would be blessed in some way through meeting me or hearing about my faith in God. Only God knew the outcome and I didn't have the energy to worry about how things would turn out.

However, this latest piece of news - that this was as good as it gets – turned my stomach so that I felt physically sick with fear. 'God – in Your mercy – hear my prayer. Please don't let me die yet. Father, please heal me by the power of the Holy Spirit. Thank You, dear sweet Jesus. AMEN.'

Chapter 24 – Waiting-room friends

Going to the hospital twice a week for blood tests, and having to wait for up to two hours in the chemotherapy waiting-room for the results, friendships were gradually formed between the people waiting for their results and those about to embark upon the next stage of their treatment.

There were times when none of us spoke to each other, each of us lost in our own thoughts. At times, particularly after I came out of hospital mid-February 2007 having had the stem cell transplant, I was so weak that I would close my eyes and sleep the waiting time away.

But as the weeks wore on, and I became stronger, I recognised some of the 'regulars' who attended each Monday and Thursday. There would pass between us a smile of recognition and a sympathetic nod. Then, maybe after a couple of weeks of smiling and nodding, one would proffer their name eliciting a response from the other person or people in the room.

Then we'd fall silent again, not wishing to intrude any further, perhaps thinking we'd strayed too far into private details. Or waiting, perhaps, for someone to break the silence with a comment or question which would provoke a statement or answer in return.

Gradually, we all became comfortable with one another and we'd exchange stories. Many of us were bald, thanks to the rigours of chemotherapy and some were sprouting new growth, while still others had wispy bits clinging on defiantly.

The upside of being bald – apart from looking like a bowling ball – was the savings on hair products. No more costly shampoo and conditioners or visits to the hairdressers. I might save hundreds of pounds, I kept telling myself, so I saw it as a temporary silver lining.

Wearing the headscarves, though, as demonstrated by the Wig Lady – well, that never really worked out for me. There was a woman in the waiting-room, Pat, who was tall, willowy with beautiful bone structure and vivid blue eyes. The way she wore her headscarf she always looked so elegant and graceful, as if she was a film star gliding on the red carpet to the latest film premier as she walked into the waiting-room.

I, on the other hand, being short and dumpy, resembled more a drag queen in panto, or a Russian peasant wringing her hands at a failed beetroot crop. So, I stuck with my little beanie hat and looked more like Benny out of 'Crossroads', and let Pat be the perfect advert for having cancer and looking glamorous.

One of my happiest memories occurred sometime in May or June 2007. I was still very bald and had recovered from the terrifying experience in March, when I caught the flu and almost died. I was very weak from this and had gone backwards in my recovery. I now needed a wheelchair, as I wasn't strong enough to walk to the pathology department to give the blood samples, and then walk up the long corridor to the chemotherapy unit to wait for the results.

Often, I fell asleep while waiting for my blood test results, discouraging any conversations with the others. But this one particular morning, we were all animated, talking to each other, and laughing loudly at various humorous anecdotes that we were sharing. One of the chemo nurses came out of the office, which was opposite the waiting-room and laughingly asked what all the noise was about. We all laughed guiltily as if having cancer should exclude us from enjoying our lives.

That occasion was a very happy time and it felt as though we were all in a disaster movie, like the Poseidon Adventure or something. There we all were, adrift in the lifeboats waiting to be rescued, amusing ourselves with tales of our medical journeys.

I went home on an absolute high because to be able to share my experiences, my doubts, my fears, and the impact of my faith, with others in a similar situation was truly liberating, and I'm sure all the others felt exactly the same way that I did. It was almost like we were attending a 'self-help' group.

With the best will in the world close family members and friends did not understand, or have the capacity to understand, exactly what I was going through. But these dear 'Waiting-room Friends', as I had dubbed them, did understand because they were going through the same things. We all understood each other's fears and, in some cases, those of us who had already gone through a particular stage that someone else was about to go through, were able to reassure them. The one thing we didn't do, however, was to share our 'horror' stories. Almost an unspoken agreement existed between us where we genuinely knew that to share these stories of 'nearly dying', or whatever, would not be helpful to any of us – whatever stage of our journey we were at.

I had become very close to several people, and I looked forward each week to meeting up with them in the waiting-room and hearing about their progress. One such friend, Val, who had Hodgkin's Lymphoma, and I really bonded. She had two dogs and I had the cats, so we were both animal lovers. We enjoyed many waiting-room hours chatting together about this and that, and nothing in particular.

We were both taking Cyclosporin, which is an immunosuppressive agent. It is used to reduce the body's natural immunity in patients who receive organ transplants. When a person receives a transplant, the body's white blood cells will try to reject the transplanted organ. Cyclosporin works by preventing the white blood cells from doing this.

For patients like Val and I who had received bone marrow or stem cell transplants, Cyclosporin might have worked by preventing the cells from the transplanted bone marrow (or stem cells) from attacking the cells of the patient's own body.

One of the side effects of Cyclosporin was that it elongates facial hair. Val and I often discussed our different treatments, whilst idly twisting the hairs on our face. We had visions of ending up like those rabbis with the long curls that are grown from their sideburns. These are called 'Payos' and refers to corners.

Of course, it wasn't as bad as that but the different changes in our bodies were scary. When you don't know what is happening internally, and the physical manifestations externally cause alarm, we had to find a way to deal with our fears. Humour was the best way.

Val always wore a beautiful wig made with real hair which looked, for all the world, as if it were her own hair. I never felt comfortable wearing my wig, so rarely wore it. Being completely bald with long curly facial hair was not a look I really wanted to cultivate for myself. After everything else that I'd already been through, did I now have to add shaving my face to my morning ablutions?

Fortunately, once we both stopped taking the Cyclosporin, the hair just disappeared on its own, and neither of us actually noticed it going.

For me, my own progress was measured in small steps, and one of these steps was that suddenly I went down to attending the hospital just once a week for blood tests, instead of twice a week.

Whilst this was great in one respect, I felt bereft in another. I would miss all the lovely people I saw on Thursdays. As I didn't go out anywhere at this point, other than to the hospital, it was a social event for me which I looked forward to every week.

I told the people on the Transport Desk, that as I would only be coming on Mondays from the following week, I would no longer need transport for Thursdays. Knowing how much I would miss my friends on Thursdays, I jokingly said that I would still come to the hospital and hang around for a bit!

The truth was that I knew I'd feel at a bit of a loss with having my Thursday mornings back again. How would I fill that time when I was used to spending a couple of hours waiting for my blood test results, chatting and laughing with my 'Waiting-room Friends'? Another truth was that I was scared. I was scared that something would be missed if I wasn't attending the hospital twice a week.

It took me a little while to realise that this was another part in the progress journey, that by reducing my visits to just once a week (where the blood tests would reveal if there were any viruses present in my blood – so nothing would get missed) I was, in fact, beginning to return to 'normal' life. Instead of being scared, I decided to embrace this wonderful freedom. I had been granted one whole extra morning back to myself to do with whatever I wanted. I may decide to do nothing with it, but the choice was mine and I felt quite heady at the thought!

Chapter 25 – Chemical analysis

I had begun researching on the Internet the alternatives to modern day things like deodorants. I had watched a programme on television, which had been very thorough in its exploration of the use of chemicals in our daily lives, and the effects that these chemicals had on the body. The programme posed the question: did we, the viewer, know that 60% of the chemicals used in beauty products and preparations leech into the skin? Following on from that, I carried out my own research based on a couple of conversations I'd had with a friend of mine called Marion. Marion had experienced breast cancer twice and had had a double mastectomy. As a result, she and her husband had adopted an organic lifestyle, growing their own fruit and vegetables and using laundry and cleaning products which were free from chemicals.

She had alerted me to the fact that many products contain parabens which, although is a preservative, is a known carcinogenic and, as a result I had tried to become more aware when I shopped for shampoos, deodorants, body lotions etc. I was becoming increasingly worried and distressed – not to mention frustrated and angry – that so many products I'd used for years ALL contain barrel-loads of parabens.

It's a shocking fact that chemicals are in every conceivable product that we eat, drink, use in our daily cleansing routines, and in our house cleaning products. And what is worse, far worse, is that there have been no studies carried out on the long-term toxicity levels of any of these chemicals.

Where do all these chemicals go? What effects do they have on the body? On individual organs in the body? On the brain? We know, for example, that smoking, drinking excess alcohol and not eating a sensible diet can cause various cancers – most of which are successfully treatable. But what about all the 'weird' cancers and different types of leukaemia where the sufferer doesn't smoke, drink and eats a sensible diet? How did they get the cancer? More importantly, WHY did they get the cancer?

Although I do not have a scientific degree, nor do I have a medical degree, I believe that it's a build-up of the chemicals in our bodies from the foods we eat, drink, etc., that are responsible. Sadly, I can't prove it – it's just my opinion and although there are many people who do agree with me, a nursing friend doesn't, and so therefore I could be wrong. But it does make me wonder.

Thanks to my friend Marion, I explored some organisations who sold organic beauty products. I bought some deodorant which is aluminium-free. Aluminium had been allegedly reported as being a contributing factor in the cause of breast cancer, although the jury is still out on the verdict, but it doesn't hurt to be aware – and therefore – careful.

The downside of some organic products is that they are fragrance free (fragrance is produced by millions of different chemicals) and therefore, in using the deodorant, there is a slightly scary moment when I think I can smell myself. I jokingly tell people that I now smell like a wart hog (which isn't true, by the way!) and that wart hogs the world over are gathering in their thousands, or it could be millions, as I don't know how many wart hogs there are throughout the world – to meet up with this newest member of their clan.

One can only hope that by careful analysis of reading labels before buying the product, one can therefore make an informed choice. There are some products that I do want to buy, and they come with parabens, so I have to make the decision as to whether or not I vitally need that product and, if I decide not to buy it, then I need something in its place. Until more manufacturers realise the dangers that the myriad of chemicals in our food, drink, cleaning products, and beauty and cosmetic products causes, the less likely we are of having a fuller spectrum from which to choose chemical free alternatives.

The government, like the manufacturers, chooses to be deaf, dumb and blind over these things, while the consumer has no choice but to continue to buy the few organic products which are available to them. The trouble with organic produce is that it is very expensive. How can this be? And why should it be? If it's not laden with chemicals and enhancements, surely that should make it much, much cheaper? You'd think so, wouldn't you? But I'm paying ten times more for my aluminium-free, wart hog smelling deodorant than my old one. Surely, that isn't fair.

People on low incomes cannot afford to buy organic food, or drink, or planet-saving products which don't contain the chemicals needed to get out those grass, blood, ink, spaghetti sauce stains from school clothes. And I've noticed that supermarkets, which have those two for one offers, never do them on organic produce. It's always on things like cheap white bread, bottles of fizzy drink, cakes, biscuits, and frozen burgers or fish fingers which are precisely the types of food and drinks that people should be discouraged from having, because there is no nutritional value in them. So, people on lower incomes are stuck between a rock and a hard place.

They may want to improve their diet, and that of their family, but they don't have the income to do it, so they take full advantage of the BOGOFFs (buy one, get one free). So, supermarkets are, in fact, perpetuating the unhealthy eating regimes which have led to the obesity crisis in the UK at the moment.

I am on a low income as well and have often chosen a cheaper alternative because it's all I can afford that particular week. But, if organic products were to come down in price, or if I did have more money at my disposal, I would buy all organic products because I do believe them to be much better for the person who uses them, and also kinder to the planet.

Chapter 26 – My own personal Goliath

On Sunday 20 April 2008 I went to church for the first time in over fifteen months. It was very strange because I woke up later than I usually do – it was nearly 8.00am whereas I often wake around 7.00 – and I did the customary things: washed up the cat bowls, gave the cats fresh breakfast, made my own breakfast, got washed, dressed etc. I wasn't rushing but I managed to get out of the house by about 10.20am. Our Sunday morning services begin at around 10.30 but I didn't hurry – I felt it wouldn't matter too much if I was five minutes late.

I arrived with seconds to spare as the uniformed groups (Scouts, Cubs and Beavers) were lined up outside the church with the Colours to march into church celebrating St. George's Day, which was on 23 April.

I sat in the back pew not wanting to get caught up in making myself known to others. I know that sounds strange, but I knew that after the service many people would come up to me and hug me because they hadn't seen me for such a long time. I didn't want to be hugged because I was still very nervous about picking up a virus or infection.

The hymns and songs we sang were just lovely and despite coughing through many of them, I did my best to worship God as honestly as I could. The sermon was based on the Reading from 1 Samuel: 17: 1 – 11; 45 – 58. Our vicar, Geoff Clarke, spoke a little bit about St. George and his origins before launching into the story of David and Goliath. As I sat there listening intently, I realised that I had been facing my own Goliath.

The seemingly impossible task of finding a man worthy enough to fight the nine-foot-tall giant, Goliath, was solved when David, a puny little shepherd, stepped forward. Saul's armies were quaking in fear at this giant. Yet, a man with no fighting experience, no armour, no sword, shield, and no battle techniques went bravely to the front of the army and stood there, facing the giant.

Naturally, Goliath mocked David and he mocked Saul for sending such a boy to do a man's job. But what no one realised was that David TRUSTED in God, and, because he had put his faith in God, God delivered. So, David put a stone in his sling, swung it round and round, and it hit Goliath full in the forehead, knocking him down. He went over to where Goliath lay and plunged Goliath's own sword into him, killing him. Then he cut off the giant's head.

As I listened to Geoff's words, I could see the events of recent weeks laid out before me. I could see that this was my own Goliath and, as insurmountable as the difficulties which lay ahead seemed to be, I had one thing on my side which I knew would help me to get through. I had my utter faith in God and, I knew that he would bring me through this next fight.

It's easy when you have a faith system to become jaded when that faith isn't being fed. I hadn't been to church for so long and, as most of my hospital clinic appointments were on a Wednesday, I couldn't go to many of the Wednesday morning communion services either. So, I felt dry and dusty. Although I had regular prayer times with God – in the morning and again in the evening, and various ongoing conversations during the day with him – I wasn't being fed spiritually. And it showed.

As Geoff's words sank into my brain, the light went on again, and my heart quickened with recognition that I was 'meant' to go to church that morning because I was 'meant' to hear this message from God (via Geoff – and the words of the songs we sang). God had chosen to speak to me, to tell me that although I felt puny and unprepared for battle, like David, I had God on my side. And if you honour God, he will fight in your corner for you.

I walked home from church with lightness in my spirit, and I smiled to myself at the knowledge that I was not alone in my 'fight'. There have been many times when I've felt so desperately alone, when it's felt as though no one truly understood how I feel or if they even care. I'm sure that hasn't been the case in reality, but that's how it *felt*. Sometimes when I wanted to talk about my feelings, the person I was talking to would try to change the subject. I realise why, and understand their frailties and weaknesses, so why can't anyone understand mine?

I would often talk to God about how I felt; expressing my fears and doubts, asking him if there was a point to all this 'suffering'. That God gave his own Son, Jesus Christ, to suffer on the Cross for each one of us made my own 'sufferings' seem very insignificant by comparison. And I knew that some of my 'Waiting-room Friends' had certainly suffered a great deal more pain and discomfort with their illnesses than I had in mine but, at the end of the day, it's all relative to your own life.

I didn't have any answers. I only knew that hundreds, possibly thousands of people throughout the world had been praying for me since the diagnosis on June 7 2006, and even though I had prayed fervently that I wouldn't have to have chemotherapy and that I would be healed *BEFORE* then, it wasn't to be.

God knows the end from the beginning. It says in Jeremiah that he has a plan to prosper us, not to harm us, and therefore I just knew that, even though I didn't understand why I still had to walk this journey, I certainly wasn't alone.

There is a wonderful poem called 'Footprints' where the writer looks back over his life and notices that, during the times when he had the most problems, he only saw one set of footprints. It seemed as if he'd been through those hard times by himself and, therefore, he questioned God: 'Lord, why when I had those times of trouble did I only see one set of footprints? Didn't you care that I was troubled?'

God answered: 'My child, it was at those times that I carried you.'

So, for a while after my lunch, I sat and thought some more about the morning's service, and God brought to mind many blessings that he'd bestowed upon me in the past. Chastened and humbled, I apologised and realised that during my times of heartache and despair, when there was only one set of footprints it was then that God had carried me.

Chapter 27 – Sunshine and smiles

Tuesday 6 May 2008 was a great day in many ways. The weather, for one thing, made it a great day. All of a sudden, the south eastern corner of the UK where I live, was bathed in glorious sunshine, and for more than a day at a time. We were hopeful that this could be the start of our summer at long last!

It was a great day for another reason. My friend and neighbour, Gary, who lives across the road from my house, came over and began to decorate my awfully dated dining room. It had last been decorated fourteen or fifteen years earlier and was looking decidedly careworn and shabby. I'd bought a new light-coloured pine table and chairs towards the tail-end of 2007, and I'd promised myself that I would get wood laminate flooring to replace the carpet, eventually – once the room had been decorated. Timmy, for some unknown reason, threw up on a regular basis and despite careful cleaning, the vomit always left a faint stain on the carpet which was really hard to remove, and I decided that laminate flooring would be a lot easier to keep clean. It's more hygienic when you have pets to have wood flooring and, as I already had it in the front room, I knew how nice and fresh it looked.

I have an old pine Welsh dresser which has aged to a dark orange and, as I couldn't afford a new one, Gary said that he'd paint it for me to give it a new lease of life. I had been pruning and editing some of the things I had on display on its shelves, but it was still cluttered with the general detritus of daily life.

For many years, every time I went abroad to Spain, I would buy a colourful jug as a memory of a good holiday. The jugs were pretty and occasionally I'd use them for little posies of flowers. But like all collectables, they gathered dust, and since I'd been at home recovering from the trials of the past year, dusting hadn't been my strong point. I decided that I would have to be ruthless and get rid of some of my 'treasures'.

On the chimney breast wall, I had a 'gallery' of pictures – maybe about fifteen or so pictures of various sizes all grouped artistically above the fireplace. They too, had gathered dust, and the ones that were higher up were difficult to reach without getting a chair to stand on.

Gary and I took them off the wall in readiness for the original wallpaper to be stripped off. I piled the pictures on the sofa in the living room at the front of the house wondering what I might do with them. The new colour scheme wouldn't be right for some of the pictures and, as I was going to have a patterned paper on the chimney breast wall now, I'd decided to put a large mirror there instead.

There is a door in the corner of the room which leads to the cupboard under the stairs. This is like the Black Hole of Calcutta! Everything that can't be found a home gets 'thrown' in there. The front part of the door had been boarded over with hardboard many years before I moved into the house, and it had always looked ugly. The house was built in 1901 and is therefore a Victorian cottage style house. Doors in those days were usually four-panel doors and covering up the panels was something that was done in the sixties and seventies to make the doors look flush.

Gary asked me if I wanted the hardboard panel removed and

the door restored to how it should be. It had a tacky plastic, nicotine-yellow handle which I was glad to see the back of, and it took Gary only a few minutes to pull the panel off.

The door was in pretty good condition apart from being a nasty almost mustard coloured, browny-yellow on the side that had been covered up. And from where the hand plates had been positioned – in two different places for some unknown reason – you could tell that the door had been painted repeatedly, without stripping off the previous coats. We decided that it would be better if we got the door stripped professionally, rather than have Gary take perhaps a day to strip it manually using a product like Nitromors, which would have meant I couldn't be in the room because it's such a strong chemical.

I looked in the Yellow Pages and found a company which wasn't too far away and arranged a time and price for the collection of the door. Gary then took the door off its hinges, removing all my coats from the inside of the door, bemoaning my lack of being able to throw things away!

I'm someone who 'collects' things, and that includes friends! But, I'm also loath to get rid of things, having the mindset that they might come in handy one day! But I hadn't really realised just how much stuff I did have in that one tiny room. It wasn't until Gary and I took the pictures off the wall, the coats off the back of the door to the cupboard under the stairs, and a few other bits and pieces, that I realised I would have to be very ruthless and get rid of most of this stuff. A new room deserves to be kept in pristine condition – lived in and enjoyed nevertheless - but in order to help me to keep it clean and easy to maintain, I would have to lose the 'stuff'.

All these different bits and pieces were found temporary

accommodation in other parts of the house, and as I moved from room to room, suddenly my house looked like a garbage truck had exploded in it. The whole house just looked so messy – I really wanted to cry. Would my house ever be tidy again? Where was I going to put everything that I decided to keep? And how was I going to lug all the excess stuff up to the charity shops because there was far too much to do it all in one go?

At the same time Gary was doing all the preparation work in the dining room, my friend Phil, who was one of my Waiting-room Friends from Queen Mary's Hospital, was in the back bedroom setting up a new scanner for me. And in the garden, Lesley, a gardener, (not my hairdresser friend), was planting up Morning Glory and sweet pea seeds, and some basil and chilli peppers as well.

I kept going from one to the other checking to see that everyone had everything they needed, and making drinks where required. I felt like I was a nursery teacher with a child in each corner of the classroom tackling different projects! It felt very strange, but in a nice way.

There was also a little two-seater sofa in the dining room which I'd had reupholstered a couple of years earlier and then, because I didn't want the cats to spoil it, I covered it completely with a throw! Garfield and Timmy had always slept on it at night and now, a couple of the other cats slept on it in their little beds, and I always felt that it had a special place in the dining room. Gary suggested that I should get rid of it because with the table and chairs in the centre of the room, there wasn't much leeway with the little sofa there as well.

At first, I was adamant that it was staying put. I'd had it for the twenty-three years I'd lived in my house and, although it didn't have any sentimental value to me, I felt that it was useful. I often sat on it when I answered the phone in the dining room, although I have to be honest and say that it wasn't terribly comfortable. But I could see that the new colour scheme and the pattern of the material on the little sofa were going to clash, and I had to make a decision!

I rang a few local charity shops and companies to see if they would like it, and then because I drew a blank there, I advertised it on a local recycling group on the Internet. www. freecycle.org is a place to advertise things wanted or things to get rid of. No money changes hands. Everything is given and received for free. The person who wants the item collects it. Much to my surprise, I had a 'taker' and a day and time was arranged for them to view the sofa.

The cat beds and throw were removed; I dusted the wooden parts and vacuumed the cushioned parts, in fact, I vacuumed and dusted until I was blue in the face and needed to lie down and rest. The hallway and dining room looked lovely (for a change), and I felt a moment's pride as the sofa sat there blushing gently after its quick make over. And then came the crushing disappointment as the person arrived and tried hard not to wrinkle their nose in disgust as they said it wasn't what they were looking for.

Smiling, as if I hadn't a care in the world, I showed them out and wished them luck with their quest. Phil (who'd been installing the new scanner for me) helped me to carry it out into the front garden where my son, David, had arranged for a work colleague to come and collect it. But, before that happened, there was a knock on the front door. Two ladies, I'd never seen before, asked if they could have it because the colours were exactly the right ones for their newly decorated living room. At last it was going to a new home where it would be appreciated and not stick out like a sore thumb. I contacted David so that he could cancel his colleague from having a wasted a journey and went back to look at the space where the sofa had lived for several years. It seemed a big space and I wondered how I could fill it!

Gary had the perfect answer. In my long narrow hallway, I had a lovely console table made of Mexican pine. It was, if I'm honest, too wide for the hallway, although it was only about eighteen inches wide, but it did clutter the hallway up and I did have more junk on its top. Gary moved it into the space in the dining room where the sofa had been – and because it was so much smaller, it just fitted there perfectly. I could now put the phone on it and a vase of fresh flowers.

The following day, Gary sent me a text to say he had a 'Man Cold' and wouldn't be coming over. I had planned to go to the Post Office anyway, and having dusted the pictures off, I put four to one side for future use and took the rest up to one of the charity shops. I was looking out of interest to see if there was anything I fancied, when I spied the Spanish jugs and some of the other non-Spanish jugs that I'd taken up a couple of weeks beforehand. I felt a warm glow on seeing them as they reminded me of holidays past, but I knew I had to be strong; I was on a de-cluttering mission and I had to get rid of a lot more stuff before the day was out. In fact, there was so much stuff it was going to take me months to go through it all and get rid of it!

Gary's 'Man Cold' lasted for several days and, although I was really sorry that he felt so unwell, it meant that I didn't have to be the 'hostess with the mostest', and I could quieten my life a bit. I was, to be honest, absolutely exhausted after Tuesday's frantic carryings-on, and although I desperately wanted the dining room to be finished, I also knew I needed to pace myself. One thing I learned from it though, was that I *could* do things other than being on the computer or lying sprawled out on the sofa. I had been up *and down* the ladder several times, stripping the wallpaper off and although that isn't technically hard work, it was very tiring for me.

I learned something else as well, and this was brought home to me when I watched a programme on television about ten young people with various disabilities. These disabilities included cerebral palsy, amputation, and profound deafness. The programme was called 'Across the Andes: Beyond Boundaries' or something along those lines. Despite their disabilities they had to work as a team to help one another get through a rain forest, up the Andes mountains, and then across a dry area before they reached the Pacific Ocean. Two of the team were in specially adapted wheelchairs which required others to push and pull them along. This journey was expected to take about a month.

I found the programme incredibly humbling, and a light bulb went on inside my head. I am *not* disabled by having leukaemia, but I have been disabled by my mind. My mind has governed my actions – or more precisely, my inaction - with the fear that I cannot do anything in case I get an infection which will put me back in the hospital. This is no way to live - in fear of living. I'm an intelligent, creative, witty person and there are many things that I can do. It's just the things that I can't do that upset and frustrate me. Instead of focusing on the things I can't do, I knew that I should concentrate on the things that

I can do, which give me pleasure.

So, I spent a satisfying afternoon rewriting the synopsis to Ollie's Diaries which first appeared on my website, and I went through some of the chapters, tweaking them a bit so that I could send the first three, plus the synopsis, to a writer friend in the US for his honest appraisal before submitting them to an agent to find me a publisher.

I thought that this current situation may be 'as good as it gets' but at least I shall have lived as full a life as I possibly can, and if I can look back and be proud of what I've achieved, then that life won't have been in vain.

Chapter 28 – Graft Versus Host Disease

We had a few sunny days in May, and I learned, to my cost, just how vulnerable my skin was since having had chemotherapy. Despite using a Factor forty sun barrier cream and being in the garden for less than twenty minutes, I still managed to catch the sun across my left shoulder and the left side of my chest.

Although it was red, it wasn't burnt, which I was pleased about, but I was surprised a few days after this event, to notice that I had a nasty rash in the same place where I'd caught the sun. When I went to bed, I dabbed calamine lotion on to it, to calm it down so that I wouldn't scratch it while I was asleep.

I wasn't sure if I was now allergic to the sun or if I was perhaps allergic to the sun cream. As I had an appointment with the consultant Haematologist at King's College Hospital the following week, I decided to ask them about it.

By then, the rash had spread throughout my body. It was particularly bad on my chest, back and upper arms, but I also had a sore mouth and had difficulty in swallowing when I first got up in the mornings. Everything I tried to eat hurt my mouth and, although I couldn't see anything out of the ordinary, it was just very sore. It felt as if everything was now going wrong.

The consultant, Dr Lim, took great care while examining me, and said that he thought that the rash and the sore mouth was something called 'Graft Versus Host Disease.' This was something we had been expecting since January 2007, when I had the stem cell transplant, because it would signify that Tony's stem cells were taking over mine.

Up until November 2007, the cells had remained disappointingly low and percentage wise, ninety-five percent were mine and only five percent were my brother's cells. The lymphocyte (white blood cells) infusions were supposed to strengthen Tony's cells, but even after three infusions, in November 2007, January and March 2008, the figures were still disappointing. And at the consultation in May, eight percent were Tony's cells and ninety-two percent mine.

Dr Lim felt slightly more hopeful that if I had got Graft Versus Host Disease, then at last Tony's cells might be fighting their corner and giving my cells a run for their money.

He called on the expert advice of Dr Anthony Du Vivier, a top dermatologist at King's College Hospital, who happened to be in the Haematology Department at the time. Dr Du Vivier peered at my skin from all angles and said that he thought it was Graft Versus Host Disease, but to make sure of his diagnosis, he wanted me to go to a building across the street from King's so that he could take a skin biopsy in theatre.

When I heard the words 'biopsy' and 'theatre' I started to panic. I have a very low pain threshold and I asked Dr Du Vivier if it would hurt. Knowing that I would have had several bone marrow biopsies, he said if the pain from one of them was on a scale of one to ten and I measured it at ten, then the pain level from a skin biopsy would only measure one out of ten. He was right – it didn't hurt because he anaesthetised the area first and then I felt a tugging sensation before he put a stitch in.

I had to take Aciclovir five times a day for ten days just

in case there were any infections, by which time I would be going back to King's College Hospital for the results of another chimerism test and the skin biopsy.

My mouth was so sore that I was told to gargle with Chlorhexadrine mouthwash again. It doesn't taste very nice and alters the way everything tastes. So, although I'd be hungry, I couldn't taste my food very well, and all drinks tasted weird. Even my favourite cappuccino sachets lost their appeal. To this day, black coffee (which I used to drink all the time) evokes memories of a morning spent vomiting into seemingly dozens of sick bowls, while I was having chemotherapy, at Queen Mary's Hospital.

As my gums felt so sore, I just nibbled with the ends of my teeth so that the food would touch as little an area of my mouth as possible.

Eating salad was absolute hell at this time because of all the different textures, shapes and sizes of the various salad vegetables I'd pile on my plate. Wanting to eat as healthily as possible I ate a lot of salad, but it was sheer agony for my mouth. Often, it would take me nearly an hour to get through a medium sized plate of salad because I'd try to nibble each vegetable carefully without it touching my gums. Because I had no saliva, food particles gathered around my gums and it physically hurt to use my tongue to try and clear everything out of the way. The constant running my tongue around inside my lips and gums reminded me of the cats when they've finished eating, and they lick their whiskers a few times to ensure they've had every last morsel of food!

I was also worried in case this 'tongue-lashing' became an obsessive-compulsive habit and, like a nervous tic, would take over and be a dominant feature of my life even when my saliva returned in the not too distant – hopefully – future.

On the 4 June I had to go back to King's College Hospital to get the results of the latest chimerism test, which I'd had two weeks' previously during May's consultation. Then, the percentage of my brother's stem cells was only at eight percent. This was not good. The results were more encouraging this time: they'd gone up to twenty percent which meant mine were down to eighty percent - a much better percentage. There was still a long way to go, but it did mean that the lymphocytes were beginning to work, at long last.

The downside of the increased percentage in my brother's cells was that the rash had spread from head to toe, and all points in between. It was an angry red rash and, when I became hot, I itched like a demented being. I couldn't stop myself – I had to scratch, and I drove myself crazy scratching all the bits of me that I could reach! Not a pretty sight! Even Timmy meowed very loudly and sat behind me on the sofa trying to nudge my hand away as I scratched my head and shoulders.

The biopsy confirmed that it definitely was Graft Versus Host Disease. I am the Host and my brother is the Graft and it looked like, finally, he was getting his own back on me for all the times I was probably horrible to him when we were growing up!

I'd seen my Haematologist consultant and he told me to wait in the waiting-room and Dr Du Vivier would come over to see me. Due to a communication problem – (i.e. there *wasn't* any communication) - I sat in the waiting-room for over an hour and a half. I went back to the reception desk and asked if I'd been forgotten.

'Oh no,' the receptionist said cheerfully, 'you haven't been forgotten. You've been waiting in the wrong place. You should have gone straight over to the Dermatology Department where they were waiting for you for an immediate appointment!'

The Dermatology Department is just across the road from the main entrance at King's so, within ten minutes (with a quick stop off to go the loo en route!), I reported to their reception area. One of the nurses, David, whom I'd met two weeks earlier when I had the first skin biopsy, came to tell me that there were four people in front of me. As it was just past 4.00pm, I imagined it would be almost five, or even later, before I'd be seen. So, I got my new book out which my friend and animal activist in the US, Jim Willis, sent me and began reading.

Within about five minutes Dr Anthony Du Vivier, came out, full of apologies at having kept me waiting, and took me straight into his den. He wanted to do another skin biopsy, so we had to go back through to the theatre where this time, skin was taken from my arm. And yes, there was another stitch! And this time, it hurt a little.

He arranged with one of the nurses, called Valerie, to have a meeting with me the following Wednesday when I had to go back to King's to see the usual consultant Haematologist. She would give me an orientation introduction into a system called PUVA, which is like a sun tanning booth. Apparently, giving the skin very short bursts of UV helps to squash the rash, but it would make me extremely photo-sensitive afterwards. Dr Du Vivier told me that I would have to 'act like a film star and wear sunglasses all the time', so I responded with: 'Can I have a couple of big bouncers to go with me then?' He laughed and said I was a very amusing woman!

It was arranged that I would go to King's College Hospital twice a week for the PUVA treatment for the next ten weeks, as there are twenty sessions in all. Because of my outpatients' appointments and blood test days at Queen Mary's Hospital, it would mean that some weeks I would be going to hospital four times a week. I was also trying hard not to miss my creative writing class which was on Fridays – so I knew I would be 'knackered'.

The day after my visit to see Dr Du Vivier, I began taking Prednisolone and believe it or not, I didn't sleep AT ALL that Thursday night. I got up at 3.45am and went downstairs to have a cool wash to try and relieve the itching and heat in my body. Knowing that I wouldn't sleep, I just went on the computer to do some housekeeping of the files in my inbox. At 6.25am I went downstairs to put the rubbish out for the refuse collectors who come around about 7.00am and, as the cats saw me through the glass panes in the dining room door, I got them some breakfast. Then I lay on the sofa and managed to sleep for about an hour and a half. I was late for my writing class, but at least I got there.

I wasn't too hungry when I left the class (which was unusual!), and I took a bus up to the local shopping centre in Bexleyheath. Even though it was 1.00pm, I still didn't feel that hungry, but I knew if I went shopping on an empty stomach I would buy all sorts of stupid comfort foods that I wouldn't normally buy, so I went to get some lunch first.

I got home about 3.00pm and put the shopping away. Normally, I would have a sleep after my writing class for about one to two hours, but that Friday I didn't feel like it, so I went upstairs to work on the computer. Even though I only had about an hour and a half's sleep in the morning, I still didn't feel all that tired so I wondered if the steroids and the new antihistamine tablets I'd been put on were something to do with that. I hoped they wouldn't send me into a hyper-drive or something. I could live without eating much (I needed to lose the weight), but I really minded very much about not getting enough sleep.

That Saturday, June 7, marked the second anniversary of the leukaemia diagnosis and then, on Thursday, it would be two years since Garfield had moved on. It had been an incredible journey, and there had been times when I had to pinch myself to believe it was all true and had actually happened. Most of the time, I'd been blessed with relatively good health with just an occasional blip along the way, so I thought I shouldn't complain too much – although the itching drove me absolutely insane. It was on the soles of my feet, the palms of my hands and everywhere else. At any one time, there were several parts of me all itching and it truly did drive me mad.

It was extreme, like prickly heat. Intense itching all over my body, including places you wouldn't expect to have a rash. Timmy, who always sat next to me on the sofa, would nudge my hands away when I went on a frenzied scratching attack. He'd yap at me as if to say 'no' like he did when he tried to prevent Garfield from coming down the stairs.

I almost broke down in tears at the consultation with the Haematologist because he knows Phil, one of my Waiting-room Friends who has the same leukaemia as me, and Phil had suffered from Graft Versus Host Disease for *over a year*! I had only had it just over three weeks and I couldn't cope.

The new treatment I would be having over the next ten

weeks would be to try and suppress the rash, but they didn't want to suppress it too much because that would, in turn, suppress my brother's stem cells and they needed to be encouraged to continue their assault. This part of the journey was not going to be easy.

PUVA works like a suntanning booth, but it felt a little like being in a microwave, and I half expected that I would have to turn round and round on a circular plate, till I was 'done'.

It was a fiendishly clever machine because it worked out the amount of time I needed to spend in it, being zapped by the UV rays. Ridiculously, or so it seemed to me, the first time I had it done, I was in there for a mere thirty-six seconds. All that preparation: I had to take two tablets two hours before the treatment began; I couldn't wear make up or perfume; and stripping down to my underwear – for just thirty-six seconds. Factor in the hour journey each way, and it seemed incomprehensible to me to go through all that for such a short, almost meaningless, amount of time.

Three days later, I went for a second burst of PUVA, this time for fifty-three seconds. Each time I went, the dose was increased slightly. Remarkably, after one session which lasted for two minutes and twenty-three seconds, Dr Du Vivier said my skin had improved considerably, so I didn't have to go for any more treatments. I had only had seven out of the proposed twenty sessions, so I'd come through another hurdle seemingly intact.

Once again, I was reminded of the Footprints poem when the writer says to God: 'When I was going through times of great trouble and stress, I noticed that there was only one set of footprints. How could you leave me at a time when I was most in need?' To which God answers, as we know: 'My dear child, it was at those times of great need that I carried you.'

When I looked back to that time, it made me well up with tears as I realised afresh the promise of God's love for each one of us, his beloved and precious children. I felt so humble that he would scoop me up in his arms and carry me through this difficult part of the journey because I couldn't walk on my own.

Chapter 29 – Missing words

Writing had always been a passion of mine, from as young as I could remember. I had a poem published in a Foyles' Junior Book Club magazine when I was ten and a half and, over the years, I had many other pieces published in various magazines. I wanted some feedback and advice on the book I was writing so, as part of the 'new me' – with spindly hair – I decided to join a local creative writing class.

Going to the class was one way of keeping hold of reality. Living once again with twice weekly hospital visits to treat my skin because of the Graft Versus Host Disease, meant that I was having to live with train timetables, setting the alarm clock to get up early, preparing lunch (if I'd remembered to take the rolls out of the freezer the night before!) to take with me, and trying to fit in the minutia of ordinary day to day life. Sometimes it was quite difficult, if not almost impossible.

So, writing was an escape. It was a way out of the sterile life sentence that having leukaemia had imposed on me, and it took me to far flung places, exotic locations, meeting dark, handsome heroes and fearless, feisty feminine heroines.

Having had cats for nearly thirty years, and studied their behaviour, I've learned a lot about them. I've had my website www.thedailymews.com since sometime in 2002 and, writing humorous stories and anecdotes based on my own cats, came easily to me. I did wonder if I could write about anything else and going to the writing class proved to me that I could.

Our tutor, Donald, a really lovely Christian man with smiling brown eyes, was a good teacher and encouraged each of the students to meet the brief that he set for homework each week. I surprised myself with some of the pieces I wrote, proving that my imagination was active, and that despite suffering from 'chemo-brain', words were still available for me to pluck and string together.

Occasionally, 'chemo-brain' would strike and I'd stare into space trying to find the word I wanted. Just as Flaubert would spend a day in search of the exquisite elusive word, I found myself spending anxious hours like a parent waiting for their rebellious teenager to come home, hoping the word would show up. Sometimes, after some word association exercises, I'd retrieve the word acting like a little lost child hiding behind a pillar from its worried mother. But, more often than not, the word remained elusive, out of sight and out of mind, lost perhaps forever in the deep recesses where chemotherapy had killed off a few too many brain cells. Then I'd have to engage in Plan B and find an alternative word. It wouldn't be as good as the word I couldn't remember; not having the same punchy meaning, perhaps, and would be a poor substitute.

The word, apologetic in its second-hand, almost inferior, status, would stare back at me from the computer screen and knew its days were numbered in the sentence I was trying to construct. There were times when, having written a substitute word, the real word would suddenly hurl itself before me, prostrate at my feet, begging forgiveness for its tardy arrival. Without gratitude or a second glance, the substitute would be yanked from its position, and the tardy arrival would be positioned smugly in its slot. But that didn't happen too often.

Occasionally, I would wake up at three or four in the morning with the missing word swimming hazily and lazily in my sleepy thoughts. If I didn't write it down, then and there, I knew I would never remember it later and the substitute would get the accolade that the missing word deserved.

I don't know if all writers go through this angst, but my work was always brilliant, until I read it out in class. Then it became a mass of self-indulgent nonsense, half-baked ideas leading nowhere. Everyone else's writing seemed so much better than mine; they read more eloquently; their writing polished. Their pieces were more descriptive and more believable. My words seemed to hang despondently in the air – like embarrassed farts outstaying their welcome after a Friday night curry.

Reading out my homework each week was probably one of the scariest things I'd ever had to do. Hearing my words – however good I might have thought them originally – suddenly now felt inadequate and inefficient in their role on the page, and I'd plummet the depths of inferiority believing I was incapable of writing anything other than futile rubbish or gibberish. I once cried on the bus home from class, because I didn't think I was good enough, and that instead of trying to be a writer, I ought to do something else and leave writing to those who could capture the readers' imagination better than I.

When one of us had finished reading out our work, Donald would always smile and ask the rest of the class for their feedback. Most would give enthusiastic praise: 'Oh, I liked it!' or 'It's good!' but there would be some who rarely commented, and I wondered if they were shy – like I am sometimes – and worried if, when they do speak, their opinion mattered.

When Graft Versus Host Disease appeared, reading out my

work was also a nightmare because my mouth was so sore and dry. For some reason I was no longer making saliva, so my lips felt swollen and tender, as if I'd overdone the Botox injections and had 'trout-pout', but on the inside of my mouth instead of the outside. My tongue felt too big for my mouth, and kept getting caught up with my teeth, and my mouth felt square with my teeth in the wrong place.

I had a saliva 'replacement' gel to apply, but it wasn't very successful, so I took to chewing gum relentlessly in a bid to try and produce saliva. When it was my turn to read, I always felt literally tongue-tied, and alternated between dribbling and spitting, although as there was no saliva, this didn't actually happen. But this is how it felt, and it also felt as if I was talking funny because without saliva, to me, I sounded strange.

Chewing gum just made my gums sorer, so I'd try not to do it for a few hours at a time, but eventually I'd give in and resume chewing again. The pain I experienced – intense at times – as the little pockets of gum broke down into the gooey chewy mix, would bring me to the brink of tears. But I'd continue chewing because, somehow, that was better than the discomfort of a dry mouth.

Being on Prednisolone (a steroid) to help suppress the rash I had with the Graft Versus Host Disease, I went into eating over-drive. I ate house-like proportions – despite the sore, dry mouth – and I had the worst sugar craving I can ever remember. Cancer feeds on sugar, so once I'd been diagnosed with leukaemia, I did my best to eat as healthily as possible, and the little sugar I did allow myself (on strawberries or raspberries, for example) I had stopped having. Virtuously, I found I didn't miss sugar at all, and although I rarely ate sweets, cakes or biscuits before being diagnosed with the leukaemia, it was no hardship to actually cease having them altogether. So, for probably twenty months or more, no sweet things passed my lips, apart from the Easter Egg.

Once I started taking Prednisolone, however, all that changed and I rampantly devoured half pound bags of Liquorice Allsorts in one go, not worrying about the surge of sugar coursing through my sugar-free veins, or the inevitable fallout that liquorice engenders. Nocturnal visits to the bathroom at 3.00am ensued. Clutching the sides of the toilet with white knuckles while not only all my insides poured forth, but it seemed the insides of half of England had gathered as well. I'd stagger out of the bathroom maybe thirty or so minutes later, a film of perspiration on my top lip, eyes dark with pain and fear, and the question hovering in my mind as to whether I should chance going back upstairs to bed in case of another 'attack'. The bathroom is downstairs and there are four cats to negotiate to get there in one piece.

For some reason if I get up in the night to go to the bathroom, the cats all congregate at their placemats in the kitchen, waiting for me to come out of the bathroom and refill their dishes with their favourite 'dish de jour', or perhaps that should be 'dish de nuit'.

I eventually stumbled back to bed, with my innards hurtling towards my knees, my stomach tightening in spasms, while my mind considered the wisdom in consuming a half-pound bag of Liquorice Allsorts. All I needed at this moment was for a missing word to jump out from behind the curtain going 'TA DA!', and I knew I would have no chance of getting back to sleep for at least another hour or more, if I was lucky.

In the early hours, just before daybreak, my best thoughts and ideas for all my writing projects would arrive. In a jumble they'd present themselves to me, smiling, proud, pleased as punch and raring to go. I gratefully acknowledged their presence but told them I'd sort them out after breakfast. I needed sleep. Lots of it. They'd grumble a bit, but continued to dance in my brain, so that quality sleep was now lost, and light sleep remained while I wrote a best-seller behind closed lids.

I woke with a start a bit later, sending the thoughts helter-skelter into the recesses of my mind. I didn't know if I would find them again but that wasn't my main concern at that moment. I couldn't swallow. I couldn't breathe. I couldn't produce any saliva to aid the swallow and I sat up with a panicked, jerky movement. I can't die with an unwritten book in my head I told myself.

Willing my mouth to move – perhaps it would set the swallow in motion – once again I feared that the constant tongue-lashings around my lips and gums might be construed as a new nervous tic inviting strangers to look at me oddly in the street. I tried not to panic and took great gulps of Vimto in a desperate bid to lubricate my mouth, swilling it round and round before swallowing. Mentally I prayed: 'Oh Lord, please don't take me like this. Not yet. Not now. I'm not ready.' Occasionally, a tear would fall as I realised that the house is in a mess, and if I'm found dead in bed, what would the neighbours say?

I would often wake up, unable to swallow, with my tongue stuck to the roof of my mouth and even having a flask of water or Vimto on my bedside table, and taking huge sips, didn't seem to make it any better. It was only at times like these – rarely at any other times – that I thought about dying. Not that I wanted to die yet. I was not quite fifty-eight and still felt I had a lot to learn and do. But I wondered if it would hurt, or if it would be swift as when my brother Ken suddenly dropped down dead. He'd been talking to two people who were out walking their dog, while doing his gardening work, in Cornwall, and suddenly we were bereft. I decided not to think about it anymore and lay down again to try and claw back another hour's sleep. It wasn't yet 6.00am, and even though it was light outside, I needed a bit more sleep.

So, I closed my eyes and asked the thoughts and ideas if they'd like to rejoin me. They're very forgiving and returned almost immediately bringing new thoughts and ideas with them.

I smiled to myself.

I slept.

Chapter 30 – Autumnal love

I first fell in love when I was about ten years old. John, a boy from my class in my junior school, walked me home on the last day of term just before Christmas. It was very romantic because it was snowing gently, and he held my books in one hand, while he held my hand with the other. He knocked on the front door and my father answered. John asked my father if he could have permission to kiss me, and my father – stifling the urge to laugh – granted his permission as seriously as the question had been asked of him.

John duly leaned over and kissed me on the cheek before leaving to make his way to his own house. That was it! Somehow, with burning red cheeks, I floated into my house and up the stairs, about three feet in the air, to look in the mirror to see if I looked any different now that I was in love and someone loved me. I was disappointed to notice that there were no visible signs that love had moved in and taken up residence.

Many years, two sons, several broken hearts later, and in my mid-fifties, I had given up the idea that I would ever find love again. Overweight, bald (courtesy of the rigours of chemotherapy), with a life-threatening or life-limiting illness, who in his right mind would ever snap me up as bargain of the week? Romantically, I had closed up shop. I decided I would concentrate my efforts on getting well, living my life as quietly and gently as possible in tune with Nature, writing my books, working on my cat website, growing herbs in my garden, and expending my energies loving my grandchildren and my cats. I was happy with that decision.

Throughout this journey I've been amazed by the attitudes of different people towards me. Some seem to gloss over the situation preferring to discuss their own major dramas ('I broke a fingernail' kind of thing), while others just stayed away. They probably believed if they didn't ask questions, they would avoid learning anything 'unpleasant', which they might otherwise have to deal with. Or, perhaps, what would be even worse – standing too close and somehow catching leukaemia from me, the 'Leper.' Whatever people felt about me having leukaemia, it was a lonely path at times, and I did long for a special person who might have shared the journey with me. There were many times when I felt very alone, scared, and a simple cuddle from someone who cared about me would have been just what the doctor probably would have ordered.

And that's how it was - for a while at least. Then Lawrence walked into my life when I least expected it. His wife, Larraine, a lovely, vibrant woman, wonderful wife and loving mother to three fantastic sons, had been one of my Waiting-room Friends and had passed away in September 2007 aged fifty-six. I had been very sad when Lawrence had told me about his loss, and surprised too, because at the time I knew her, she had looked relatively well. Of the two of us, I would have thought I was the one who wasn't going to come through, as I was pretty sick at the time, and I did wonder if I was going to survive or not. It just goes to show that one shouldn't judge someone by their appearance because there is no way to tell what's going on inside their bodies.

Every couple of months I bumped into him at the hospital

when we both had to have blood tests. He had suffered a major heart attack in May 2003, and his heart had stopped several times. The hospital staff managed to resuscitate him, but while a stent was being inserted, he had a massive stroke. It took him a year to learn to walk again and he was slightly impaired down the left-hand side of his body. He had to take Warfarin to thin his blood and had to have regular blood tests – which is how we came to meet up every once in a while.

We usually said a couple of words to each other and he always asked how I was feeling. One time we had a coffee and a chat while I was waiting for hospital transport to take me back home again. He appeared painfully thin, and his face was gaunt. In his grief, he had virtually stopped eating and was waiting for death so that he could be with Larraine. He spoke at length about Larraine's cancer and all the dreadful things she'd endured. The Macmillan nurse had told him, about six months before she died, that her organs were beginning to fail. He had kept the burden of that information to himself, not knowing if Larraine knew herself, but they didn't talk about it, and he discussed it with no one.

We exchanged phone numbers, and I said I would be happy to go out to have a coffee with him if he ever found himself at a loose end. I knew it was still too early for him to even consider going out with anyone else, as he was grieving but, in offering him the hand of friendship, I wanted him to know that someone cared about him even though I wasn't looking for a romantic relationship.

Since I was still tied up with going to King's College Hospital, several times a week, for treatment for the EBV virus I had in my blood, and then catching shingles the following month, I was in no fit state to go out with anyone – plus I didn't have the time. I was going backward and forward to both hospitals a couple of times each week, and if the truth be told, I didn't think he would even look at me with any kind of interest. I was sure that he wouldn't want to get involved with someone else who had a serious illness to contend with, having been through the traumatic time he'd experienced with Larraine.

Several months passed, and every now and then Lawrence would telephone me to see how I was doing, and we'd have a little chat. He was going out and about and trying to get on with his life and make sense of things. He asked if I'd be interested in visiting National Trust properties in the Kent area when I had any spare time. As I'm a culture vulture, and love period properties with tons of history attached to them, I readily accepted.

It sounds dreadful now in retrospect, but I could only see him on a monthly basis to fit around my hospital appointments and the infernal twice weekly blood tests. In hindsight, this was probably a good thing, because the friendship began very slowly and built up gradually. I think, had we seen each other several times a week right from the beginning, the relationship may have floundered.

Our first outing was to Bodium Castle in East Sussex. Thanks to GVHD, I had a rash from head to toe, and I was unable to wear make-up or perfume because of the PUVA treatments I was having twice a week at King's College Hospital. I felt very unfeminine. We sat at a little outdoor café having coffee and cake, while the little sparrows and starlings hovered nearby waiting for crumbs.

One beautiful day in mid-July, with the bluest of skies,

caressed by gentle, white puffball clouds, and the sweet sounds of birdsong in the trees, we went to Ightham Mote. It's a stunning fourteenth century, Medieval, moated manor house in our own county of Kent, with lots of history and a wonderful atmosphere. There is a steep slope leading down to the main entrance and, as I was wearing sandals, I was worried that I might fall over or slip. I asked Lawrence if I could hold his hand while we walked down that bit, he said 'yes', and took my hand in his. Immediately, I felt a frisson of electricity that took me by surprise. Unknown to me, he had felt it also, but neither of us said anything at the time.

My feelings for Lawrence were getting stronger and deeper each time we saw each other. We never held hands apart from that once; and we never kissed. There was no bodily contact at all, yet I knew I was falling in love with him. I never said anything to him to encourage his feelings for me because, although many months had passed by this time, I still felt it was inappropriate to 'get involved' with him in a romantic sense. I hadn't had a relationship for about seven or eight years and the last thing I wanted to do was to misread 'the signs', make a fool of myself, and get hurt. I needed all my energy to fight my own battle to stay alive. I couldn't risk getting hurt, expending energy that I didn't have, crying myself to sleep each night, while going through the rigours that unrequited love would throw at me; the big gaping pit in the stomach; the feeling sick because I couldn't eat; the sleepless nights etc. Been there, done that, got the tee-shirt – didn't want to go through it all again – not at my age, thank you very much.

Unknown to me, Lawrence was having those feelings as well. We never discussed our feelings, but we always enjoyed our days out together. We always had a good time with each other, laughing a lot, enjoying finding out about the historical side of things when we visited these National Trust properties and having some very nice meals in some lovely country public houses or restaurants.

There was something about him that made my stomach flip every time I saw him, or when I knew I was going to see him, it was the anticipation that would send me all a-flutter. He was tall; 6'2', with long grey hair and a neatly trimmed beard. But it was his eyes that drew me to him; brilliant blue, sparkling and, coupled with a boyishly impish smile, I could see that he had probably been a little mischief-maker when he was younger. His eyes would crinkle at the corners when he smiled or laughed, and he was so good looking. I wondered what in Heaven's name he was doing with someone like me.

Lawrence made me feel very feminine even though I wasn't very feminine in my appearance. My eyes were very sore, so I couldn't wear eye make-up, my nails were very brittle and kept breaking, so I couldn't wear nail varnish – both a legacy of having chemotherapy. I used to have pierced ears but had to take my studs out when I went into hospital to begin the treatment. The holes had since closed up and there would have been a risk of me getting an infection if I'd had them re-pierced.

At 5'4', I felt I was dealt a cruel hand in the height department – for my weight, I should be at least 8'7' tall which is why it looked as if there was more of me than there actually was. If I was 8'7' tall, the body parts would be spread out considerably, and there would be no need to feel like a Sumo wrestler's ideal partner. Being overweight, I wore clothes that didn't show off my curves – I tried to hide as much as possible, and most of the time, I felt like a little blob that probably looked more manly than womanly.

I hadn't bought any new clothes in a long time, apart from the six pairs of pyjama bottoms I wore in hospital during the day, with six coordinating baggy tee-shirts, which enabled the nurses to have easy access to the Hickman Line to feed the chemo through. I'd forgotten how to be feminine, and I was amazed that Lawrence could see through the little unfeminine 'bloblet' in front of him, and found some spark of interest which ignited, over time into a full-blown blaze of ardour.

Factor in, as well, that when we first started going out to National Trust properties, I was covered head to foot in the rash, and was attending King's College Hospital twice a week for PUVA treatment. I couldn't have felt less ladylike or feminine and, yet, he saw through all that, which surprised me.

It was probably around my birthday in the August that we first kissed – I'm not sure now – but it was a kiss that was gentle, tentative, and blew our minds. Again, neither of us said anything about how we were feeling – which, on reflection, I think was just as well. I was already nervous about getting involved with Lawrence in case he hurt me and having convinced myself that I was thoroughly unlovable and unfeminine, I didn't think he would really fancy me anyway – that we were just being friends. Lawrence sensed my nervousness and didn't act in any way that was inappropriate. But my birthday kiss had set the train in motion, and once on track, it was pretty hard to stop it!

Several more months passed and, one or two kisses later, we both came to realise ours was more than a simple friendship. In truth, it was some little while before I'd feel able to tell Lawrence the way he truly made me feel, falling in love being something I never dreamed I'd experience again. Yet to be honest, by this time, I couldn't imagine my life without him. I'd known he liked me a lot, we were so easy together, but remained in the dark as to how deep his feelings really were. I felt too frightened to ask, for I knew how deeply, and how much he'd loved his wife, and to commit to a relationship might feel like betrayal. Therefore, I kept my emotions to myself, forever patient that the love of my life might soon be ready to love again.

And slowly having someone to care for me, I started to blossom. Once I'd finished the PUVA treatment, and Dr Du Vivier had given me the go-ahead, I attempted to wear mascara and eyeshadow. My hair, which had grown back tabby-cat grey, I decided to have coloured and highlighted, which actually made me look a lot younger. I had my ears pierced again and began to wear nail varnish, occasionally. I began to buy new clothes – tentatively at first, because I was unsure of what style I should wear to suit my unwomanly shape. One of the biggest changes was that, slowly, I began to lose weight; first joining a gym and going once or twice a week in between all my hospital visits, and then by joining Weight Watchers.

Like a butterfly waking up from a slumbering chrysalis, unfolding its wings to let the warmth of the sunshine heat them so that it could fly, the new woman inside me began emerging. This slightly more confident person came to life; no longer seeing herself as a 'bloblet', but as a sexy, vivacious, curvaceous woman not only in love with life, but in love with a wonderful man who loved her in return.

I often marvel at the way things work out. Had I been healed before having chemotherapy, I would never have met all my Waiting-room Friends. I would never have met the people in the ambulances, on the way to and from the hospital – many of them taught me to embrace life, to live it to the max, and not give up regardless of any limitations or trials which may come my way. And, most importantly, I never would have met Lawrence. Despite living only a few miles apart from each other for several years, we'd never bumped into each other before – so in a way, it was serendipity that we finally met.

Lawrence endured probably the worst experience of his life, but through that tragedy we got together, and eventually fell in love. Who would have ever thought that could happen? At the age of fifty-eight I was glowing, inside and out, like an eighteen-year-old; fortunately, I didn't have a face full of zits, like many teenagers, to cope with on top of my already sizeable inferiority complex. I found myself smiling all the time, and there would be times when I would be thinking something, and Lawrence would voice it – word for word – or vice versa. We were very in tune with each other and shared many common interests.

I recently read in a book where the heroine meets up with a man she had loved thirty-five years previously, when they'd been teenagers. In this particular part, he tells her that before they're born, their soul splits apart, and half of it is given to someone else. So, all their lives, they spend their existence looking for the person with the other half. If they're lucky enough to find that person, then their soul can say 'At last, I can rest. I have found my missing half.' This is exactly how I feel about Lawrence, and I know how he feels about me; it's as though we are two halves of one heart, each beating in time with the other.

I was overflowing with happiness; it leaked out of my every

pore, and although I had always considered myself a fairly happy and contented person before meeting Lawrence, I realised just how much I had been missing by not having a special person in my life. Now – I had my own special someone, and he made the world a better place just by being in it and sharing it with me. I was so truly and utterly blessed.

It had been a long time since John, my first love, had made that ten-year-old me float up the stairs and now, here I was spending every day floating three foot above the ground with a truly wonderful man. He once told me that he was a broken man trying to put himself back together again. I know that I have been instrumental in helping Lawrence to achieve this, but he has done far more for me than he will ever know. I sincerely hope that John found and went on to make his own special person float with love for him.

Who would have thought that my life changing in June 2006, with the leukaemia diagnosis would bring about such a wonderful, positive and unexpected outcome of falling in love!

Chapter 31 – Feline therapy

Dust particles danced as a shaft of sunlight spread like a river across the floor. Two of my three remaining cats, Ollie and Billy, lay nose to tail basking in the warmth of an early March sun, which was still feeble in strength after a long hard winter. They were fast asleep, ears and feet twitching as they dreamt of who knows what. I love the fact that cats seem to find the best spots for taking a nap, and sun puddles are the absolute best. I wanted to know what that felt like, so I lay down on the floor alongside them and closed my eyes. The warmth of the sun reached my face and it felt good. I rested and let the healing sun work through my body. I do love this time of year when everything starts waking up, shrugging the sleep from tired winter eyes and getting ready to put on their party frocks for the summer!

As I marvelled while they slept, tears pricked at my eyes and I blinked rapidly to stop their flow. Life was good and I was glad to be alive. It had been a tumultuous journey and frankly, I wasn't sure that I'd come through it alive and in one piece. Putting my cats in the cattery while I tried to regain my strength was one of the hardest things I'd ever had to do. It broke my heart that, at a time when I most needed them, I had to let them reside in a foreign environment. They must have wondered what was going on. I did explain to them that I was sick and that they would be coming back, but cats live in the present, they wouldn't have any concept of what the future held in store for them or me.

It is said that cats are angels who come into our lives to nurture, love and protect us. Over the thirty years that cats have shared my life and my home, this has been proven time and time again.

My first two cats, ginger brothers, Garfield and Biggles, demonstrated their love and concern for me when they were only about five or six months old. I arrived home after a particularly bad day at work and sat at the table with my head on my arms and cried. They got up on the table and began nudging my face until I looked up. Continuing their gentle head butts, I saw the looks of concern on their faces, so I held them both to me and felt their purrs vibrate through my chest.

I didn't realise it then, just how in tune with my emotions and my health they were, but as the years rolled on and other cats joined us, I was to be the recipient of their unconditional love many times over.

Another time they showed this wonderful love for me was when they were about seven years old. I had just taken on an eight-week-old kitten that I'd named Charlie. He was a little imp, climbing up the curtains, the wallpaper and anything else within his grasp. A week after Charlie arrived, I went down with the flu. I lay on the sofa each morning and slept until it was time for Charlie's next meal. Biggles and Garfield both lay either side of me, but Charlie thought his role in my recovery was to entertain us. He did this by climbing up the curtains, and walking along the curtain rod, collecting a moustache of dust just under his nose.

Letting go of one paw, he hung off the top of the curtains as if he was waving to us. Looking like a feline Errol Flynn, he grinned at us before abseiling down the curtains to land in a saucer I had balanced on my knees. That set the saucer in motion and he tobogganed down my shins, turned left at my feet and sped off, landing on the carpet, still sitting upright in the saucer.

The whole episode took only a few seconds, but he looked up at me as if to say: 'That was good!' Meanwhile, Garfield and Biggles looked on horrified; they never did anything like that.

I remembered back to another time when I had seven cats and being in a severe relapse with the ME (Chronic Fatigue Syndrome), I had decided to lie on the sofa bed in the back bedroom one morning to have a sleep after breakfast. There were road works going on at the front of the house, so I knew it would be quieter in the back room. Garfield and Timmy were already on the bed waiting for me. Billy, Sam, Ricky, Charlie and little Ellie had all gone out in the garden after breakfast, doing whatever it is that cats have on their daily 'to do' lists.

I fell asleep with Garfield and Timmy lying next to me not noticing when, one by one, the others joined us, lying as close to me or, as near to me, as possible.

I was aware, however, despite being fast asleep, of the different purring sounds each cat made. Lulled into a peaceful sense of security, I slept on for a couple of hours.

The cats' purring didn't cease for one second, and I can remember waking up feeling energised as never before. I later wrote in a Mewsletter, which I sent out to my subscribers, that purring should be available on prescription because, surely, it had therapeutic and healing benefits. I received a flood of emails telling me about two different cats' purr CDs, so I bought both. The first one I didn't like very much as there were storms, rain, and synthetic music which almost drowned out the cats' purrs, and I only listened to it once. The second one, however, I loved, and I listened to it several times, particularly when I was in hospital because it totally relaxed me.

Jack Stewart, who made the CD, became a friend and his cat, Jimmy, wrote a regular monthly column for my website on mind, body and spirit matters. So far, Jack and his friend, Jeff Moran, have created two Cats' Purrs CDs, both of which are wonderful; both are totally relaxing and, when I listen to them, not only am I rested and feel relaxed, but if any of the cats are in the room with me while I'm listening to the CDs, they also seem to be relaxed.

I've seen documented proof of the benefits of cats' purring and, on my website, I have articles to substantiate these claims. Cats' purring can be as soft as a tiny, almost inaudible whisper, or as loud as a tractor. The loudest recorded cat's purr by a domestic cat is 67.8 db(A) and was achieved by Merlin, owned by Tracy Westwood at her home in Torquay, Devon (UK) on 2 April 2015 (Guinness Book of World Records).

Scientists never quite understood why a cat purred because it seemed a random act. If a cat is stroked and petted by his owner, who is also whispering words of love, the cat starts purring. Does this mean that the cat responds to soft soothing sounds to elicit that purr? Yet, it's been documented that if a cat has been hurt in a road traffic accident and is taken to the vet, he will be purring. The vibration of a cat's purr sets the healing in motion and, believe it or not, a cat will automatically start purring to mend broken bones. That is why I felt so energised when my seven cats lay all around me and I had stereophonic purring. My body responded to the vibrations of their purrs.

In October 2004, I had major abdominal surgery and, when I came out of hospital, it was with the proviso that I remain on bed rest for one full month, and then partial bed rest for the second month. Of all the cats, (I had six at the time), Garfield and Timmy were the only two who chose to lie down with me each day on the sofa. Each morning, I'd get up and prepare the breakfasts for the six cats before getting my own ready. Then I'd get washed, then dressed, and head to the sofa in the living room, the pillow and duvet already in place, waiting invitingly for me to just climb under and rest.

Every morning, after their breakfast, Garfield and Timmy would both go straight to the living room and would wait patiently on the sofa for me until I joined them. The other four cats would go out or go upstairs, about their business, and a couple might join us after a few hours, but my two constant carers were always Garfield and Timmy.

They would always lie right next to me and their purring would reverberate through my body. My surgery had been the removal of a very large ovarian cyst, plus my ovaries had been removed. Surgery hadn't been that simple, though, as scar tissue from previous abdominal surgeries had built up and my internal organs had fused, and to quote the surgeon's words: 'You were in a bit of a mess in there.'

What should have been a routine forty-minute operation took more than five hours to complete, and I had been cut from my belly button right round to the 'next-door neighbour's' as I prefer to put it.

Amazingly, none of my cats ever tried to get on my stomach while I'd be lying down. If any one of them got on my lap, he would always sit a little way away from my abdominal area, more towards the edge of my knees as if, instinctively, he knew.

After one month of being on full bed rest, I decided to try and move around a little bit, so after lunch, I'd stay up and perhaps walk around the garden to get some exercise, or I'd go upstairs to work on my computer. Timmy and Garfield always seemed to know what I was going to do before I knew it myself.

This was brought to mind when, after the second month of partial bed rest, I decided one morning that I wouldn't lie on the sofa, I would go for a walk to the local post office. Without any indication of my intentions, both Garfield and Timmy went straight upstairs to the spot in the back bedroom, which they usually occupied each day prior to my going into hospital. I hadn't said anything to them, but they instinctively knew.

When Garfield had told me, back in June 2006, just five days after my diagnosis, that it was time for him to move on, I think he knew that Timmy would take care of me. Garfield had been my constant companion for just over twenty years since he and Biggles had arrived at eight weeks old. Whether he knew what was in store for me, I don't know. He had many health problems which I helped him with daily. Maybe he knew that I wouldn't be able to continue with his care, and moving on, was his last unselfish act of love for me. I had five other cats at the time, and he knew I would be in safe paws.

I realised then that cats are very intuitive, and now, continuing my journey with leukaemia, they knew before I did that I was getting better. In the same way, about six months before Timmy died, he started to do other things in the mornings, instead of waiting for me on the sofa where I always had a nap after breakfast. It took me a while to realise that he knew what I was just beginning to grasp; that I was, in fact, getting better.

He knew even before the consultants at the hospitals told me – my blood tests were showing that all the components of Tony's stem cells were beginning to reach the desired levels, and that I was almost – not quite – out of danger.

When I finally sussed this out, my attitude changed subtly and I began to write more, work on my website more often, and just deal with housework and other household things that had slid because I was always too tired and, therefore, needing to rest.

Timmy had his own health problems, yet it was as though he was taking care of me and making sure that I was all right before he succumbed to his own illness.

I said my heart-breaking goodbyes to Timmy in March 2009. He had a serious heart problem and refused point blank to take the pills prescribed by Kevin, our wonderful veterinarian surgeon. Timmy and I had several discussions about the merits of him taking the medication, but I told him the choice was, ultimately, his. I didn't want to have to struggle with him, and stress us both out, three times a day. Timmy made his own choice. Whatever time he had remaining, I wanted to make sure that it would be as stress-free as possible. It seemed so unfair – and yet, in an odd way, quite fitting – that the cat whose heart was as big as a lion's, should lose his own life because of incurable heart problems. I miss him, Garfield and Ricky so much. They all gave me so much love and affection that I doubt this journey would have been the same without having my beautiful cats around me.

My journey began in June 2006, and what a journey it has been. I have met the most wonderful people, whom I would never have encountered, had my journey not occurred. People, who just by a simple word, gesture, behaviour, personality or positive outlook have enriched my life in so many ways, and I have been humbled by the response of my subscribers. Prayer Warriors throughout the world who have prayed constantly for me, for not just a moment, but for the many months and years this walk with leukaemia has taken me. And I'm so grateful to every single one.

I began this experience with six beloved cats: Garfield, Billy, Timmy, Ricky, Sam and Ollie and now I have Billy, Sam and Ollie by my side, losing first Garfield, then Ricky and then Timmy. The loss of each cat leaves a palpable pain in the pit of my stomach. They may have been small in stature, but their personalities were lionesque. It is said that domestic cats are 'living room lions.' My cats certainly measured up to this statement. I believe that all our souls are connected and that, one day, we will be together again.

I also began this journey as a single lady, but now I have a wonderful life partner who is also beginning another journey of his own. When he married his adoring wife, Larraine, back in 1972, he didn't expect to be the one to survive when they had joint health issues. And he didn't expect to ever meet another woman that he would even like, let alone fall in love with. And I, full of my own insecurities, wondered what I could possibly have to offer any one and, never in a million years, did I expect that going through this process would I meet a man whom I would love with such a passion that my heart constantly feels as if it's on fire – and no, I know it isn't heart burn!

I marvel because God, who knows the end from the beginning, brought Lawrence into my life when we both needed a friend. In a small way, I have helped him mend the broken pieces of his life while he, in turn, helped to mend the broken reed that I was. He made me realise that I am a woman who is very worthy of being loved and valued for so many things, that I never thought about myself. His great influence and encouragement with my continuing battle to lose weight; my writing projects and the exorcism of my own demons from many years ago, keeps my spirits buoyant.

And all those millions of prayers for me that were uttered in the months after diagnosis for healing – well, God knew what was in store, didn't he? I had hoped that I would have been healed before having chemotherapy. Not wanting to go through the rigours of such toxic treatment to my body but, had I been healed, I would never have met Lawrence and, who knows what road my life would have taken, or where I might have ended up?

Life is beautiful. Life can be cruel. Life can be too short for some and too long for others. But my life has begun again quite unexpectedly, and I am surrounded by love – which I neither thought I deserved nor expected. And being loved by a wonderful, caring and loving man has opened up my eyes to such great possibilities. Despite being inhibited by some of our health issues, we enjoy exploring the beautiful Kent countryside, the roads of which are reminiscent of those very same roads that I cycled along in my dreams before I started chemotherapy.

In our sixties, we realise that we've probably had the best of our lives already, and it's unlikely that Lawrence and I will be blessed with the thirty-odd years of married life that he shared with Larraine. But I live with the hope that one day, when we get to the right moment, we will join our lives together for the rest of our time remaining.

His little dog, Mason, and my three cats, Billy, Sam and Ollie are learning to accept each other – and maybe we will learn some lessons from them, who knows? But I do know that when this journey began, I had no idea how it would pan out. I know that my faith kept me strong, and I didn't doubt God's intention for one moment. I knew from Scripture that, whatever the outcome, it would be the best outcome for me. And I was ready to accept that.

Chapter 32 – One thousand days

On the chimney breast wall, in the back bedroom I use as an office, I have three pictures of cats doing various things. The picture in the middle is larger than the other two and shows a kitten hanging off the end of a broken branch.

I initially liked this picture for the quirky humour it portrays - like someone slipping on a banana skin type of humour. You laugh at their misfortune, but you wouldn't if it were happening to you! But I'm someone who sees a deeper meaning behind the simplest of things and, before long, I discovered a lot more in my cute picture of the kitten holding on for dear life.

Like all young – of any species – there is a wide-eyed innocence and an insatiable appetite for adventure, for discovery, for exploration and realisation. And this kitten, with his bright eyes wide with a mixture of fear: 'What have I got myself into now?' perhaps, and the realisation that a 'whoops' moment is coming up, is the epitome of finding out things the hard way!

Life can be a fragile existence for some, but for those with a tenacious spirit, holding on can make all the difference between life and death. Like the leaf which stoically remained on the tree across the road from my hospital ward, despite the dreadful winter weather we were having, that leaf filled me with hope.

Is the glass half empty or half full? I only ask this question because the choice of answer can mean a life of potential, the fruition of one's hopes, dreams and aspirations, or the cessation of any expectancy, motivation or drive.

Thursday 22 October 2009 was the 1,000th day since my stem cell transplant. My 1,000th day! Who would have thought it? Not me, that's for sure. My 1000th day was certainly a day to celebrate. Thanks to my younger brother, Tony, who generously shared his stem cells with me, I am here today. There had been a time, however, when – during those 1,000 days, and the months leading up to it – I didn't know if I would ever get better. And when I caught the flu while in hospital, I didn't think I would make it. Even now, when I think back to the very worst of those times, it's still hard to get my head around just how ill I really was. Although I looked pale, I didn't look gaunt or ravaged as some cancer patients do. I was still overweight and looked quite robust and relatively healthy.

I can't say, for sure, how I felt at having arrived at this milestone in my life. It's not every day you are suddenly and acutely aware of the importance and significance of 1,000 days. I can only think of this in terms of the film: Anne of a Thousand Days - and we all know what happened to her. Fortunately, I didn't lose my head, but I did lose my heart to the most loving, caring, gentle and kindest of souls. It's still a source of great wonderment and amazement to the pair of us, the day when we finally bumped into each other several months later at the hospital after his wife had passed away.

The enormity of even saying the words out loud – 'One thousand days' – was hard to get my head around. I don't think there are many of us who count in such ways; I know I certainly hadn't up until that moment. In fact, I didn't even know that it was my 1,000th day until the consultant told me. I would have been blissfully unaware of such an auspicious date had it not been for him. He'd been explaining that the further I get away from the transplant date, the better chance I had of the leukaemia not returning. Once I reached five years' post-transplant, he said, there is only a one percent chance of it coming back. I flipped that over and told myself that meant there was a ninety-nine percent chance that it wouldn't.

Since being diagnosed with leukaemia, I am much more aware of what life has to offer, in particular, *my* life. I have discovered that living is far preferable to me than the alternative. Some of the people I met in the hospital waiting-room didn't have the opportunity to reach their full potential; their lives were cut short, only half-lived, their dreams only half-realised.

What has this to do with my picture? Sometimes I find myself at the end of a branch, out on limb, with no end in sight, and a long drop ahead below. I hold on for dear life, praying for all my worth that I will be spared to live another day, another thousand or more days if I am blessed. I wish to make my mark on this ever-changing world, that my journey and experiences will matter to someone, somewhere, and make a life-changing impact on someone's life, so that they are challenged beyond their boundaries or comfort zone.

Having found my soul mate in the autumn years of my life, I don't want it snatched away before I have lived and breathed the scent of a love returned, the private look and quiet smile that lovers share, fingers entwined and long giddy kisses. So, like the kitten in the picture, I am holding on with a tenacity that finds its strength from some inner reservoir unknown to me before now, because suddenly, life is so important to me and how I live it, and for how long, is now important to someone else.

Sometimes, we go through unspeakable tragedies, times of

hardship, times of loss, and it seems so unfair. This reminded me of a tale about a piece of embroidery. 'How ugly,' the pessimist cries, when looking at the side with the tangled knots, dangling ends and untidy bits. 'But look what happens when you turn it around,' says the optimist, revealing the true beauty of the intricate embroidery. 'See how beautiful it is,' he marvels. 'We need the tangled knots, dangling ends and untidy bits in life to remind us of the beautiful things we get when we least expect it.'

When tragedy has struck, sometimes, out of the deep sorrows of the heart, love – like a tender bud – can take root and grow again when we least expect it.

Chapter 33 – Reflections

One thing I've noticed over the years of living with cats is their innate ability to just be. We humans are always 'doing'; we rarely take time out to 'be'. Even if we sit on the sofa to watch television, we think we're resting, but we're amassing the images that are flickering on our television sets. We need to sit and do absolutely nothing.

From my office window in the back bedroom, I could see Sam sitting on the garden path. He stayed in the same position for ages; I couldn't tell from my position whether he was actually looking at something or whether he was just in the moment. Cats don't think about yesterday, they don't think about tomorrow; they have no regrets about what they didn't achieve in the past, and they don't worry about what they hope to accomplish in the future. They just live in the present, the here and now.

When I was in hospital, I spent a lot of time praying. Most mornings I would do my Bible study before breakfast if there was time, if not, I would try in between all the constant interruptions. But one thing that came to light, over and over again, was the phrase: Be still and know that I am God.

This means not worrying about anything but, just rest in the moment and allow God to do what he does best. And there are times when it might seem that he isn't doing anything, but that's when things are being put into place for us to reap the benefits and rewards at a later time – when the time is right for us to receive it.

Warren Eckstein said: 'In the beginning, God created man, but seeing him so feeble, he gave him the cat.' And I think this is true, and I thank God he did give us the cat! All animals can teach us things if we just allowed them to, but for some reason, Man seems to think he has to dominate and control everything and everyone he comes into contact with. I personally believe that if we just allowed our minds to open and let the wisdom of the animals into our hearts, the world might just be a better place. Native American culture embraces the wisdom and teachings of all wildlife. They respect the quality each animal possesses and will try to emulate the characteristics of that particular animal, believing that they will become a better person if they embody the character and personality traits of that animal.

I have learned a lot from my own cats. They have been great – and very patient – teachers. I have learned that it's perfectly ok to sit and do nothing every once in a while. The world didn't end if I didn't do the ironing or clean the bathroom. If you watch a cat, you will notice that he will sit and stare at seemingly nothing, his ears will be twitching and picking up information from the sounds around, but he will keep his body perfectly still.

My friend, Gerald Schiffhorst, says in his book 'Writing with Cats' '… in their wordless world, cats know that silence is not the absence of sound; it is about presence. It is being suspended in the eternal present, outside of time; this is what the great mystics have written about. I do not claim that Lizzie (his own cat) is a great mystic, but she has the gift of being silently, fully in the present, and open to the presence of the spirit.'

He goes on to say: '… Like other felines, Lizzie has no sense of the past; she lives in a world in which there are no clocks or days or years, only the constant, timeless moment. She does not bother reviewing past problems or worrying about the future, which is as unreal and irrelevant to her as the past. This is the state of mindfulness that is the aim of Eastern and Western spiritual masters: the quality of focusing intently on the reality of the present. Writers achieve this type of self-transcendence often with great effort and then usually for only short periods. Cats, however, have this talent and seem to possess it to a more heightened degree than other animals. Rather than do anything that we humans identify as productive activity, they simply are.'

Watch a cat the next time he wakes from sleep. First, he will stretch out his front legs and then stretch out his back legs before deciding whether to go out in the garden to toilet, or use a tray if he's an indoor cat; or whether to go and see if his food bowl is full. How many of us stretch when we get up in the mornings? I know I don't usually, but on watching my cats do it, I figured if it's good for them, then it must be good for me. And surprisingly, I do feel better after having a good stretch but, if I forget to do it, then I do feel sluggish and, somehow, smaller. Stretching out is good for the spine so that I stand taller.

Cats will only eat what they want. They rarely overeat, and they will eat little and often. How many dieticians have told us that it is much better to eat several smaller meals, evenly spaced throughout the day, to keep glucose levels on an even keel? Yet how many of us encompass that idea? Some skip breakfast – the most important meal of the day; eat sugary snacks until lunch, and then have a blow out at lunch time, feel sluggish all afternoon, and think the key is to eat more sugary snacks to perk themselves up, before having another blow out meal for supper. Cats don't eat until they feel uncomfortable, like most of us do. They eat what they need, when they need it, no more, no less.

And then there is exercise. Okay, so cats do spend up to 18 - 20 hours a day asleep, and I'm not suggesting that we humans do that. But while sleeping, they conserve energy. If their humans are out of the house all day, they sleep because there isn't anything else to do in the meantime. And, if there isn't any fresh food available, sleeping saves their energy levels until such time as they are fed again.

It all makes perfect sense to me. So, cats stretch after a good sleep, they eat small meals on a regular basis, and they exercise in short bursts. Why spend money on health and fitness gurus paying them to tell you what your own cat has been advocating for years for free!

Epilogue

It's now June 2019. My journey began thirteen years ago, and there have been many changes along the way. To mark my tenth anniversary of the diagnosis of Acute Myeloid Leukaemia, I hosted a coffee morning in aid of Macmillan Cancer Support on 30 September 2016. Several of my friends from Slimming World turned up, some of whom had made delicious cakes to add to my own, and we tucked in.

The irony of what we were doing was not lost on me, either. Ten ladies, some lapsed from attending Slimming World as I had, filling their plates with the naughtiest cakes – but all for a great cause.

At lunch time, and probably with the remains of chocolate cake around my mouth, three of the ladies accompanied me to my hairdressing salon, where my stylist, Glen, was about to shave my head. All the money raised went to Macmillan Cancer Support.

2017 was a year for celebrations; I celebrated ten years of the stem cell transplant, and followed by ten years of surviving CMV, MRSA and the flu, and finally, ten years of being in remission.

Each year I say to myself that I'll take part in the Race for Life, which is for cancer survivors or in memory of those who sadly passed away, but I'm not fit enough yet to do that. My knees hurt, and I have chronic back pain, and permanent sciatica down one leg. I can't walk far, and I always felt guilty for not giving anything back.

But this time, having hosted the coffee morning and then having my head shaved, I felt as if I celebrated those ten momentous years in my own inimitable style. Many of my friends have said how brave I was, some even thought I was foolhardy, but I think I'm neither. I lost my hair down the plughole of the shower thirteen years ago, but this time, I had a little bit of fuzz, left so I wasn't completely bald.

Health wise, I do have ongoing problems, some of which are still being investigated and some of which I've had to learn to live with. Each time Lawrence and I go on holiday abroad I always get a chest infection. This is either from the flight or being in, and around, people who smoke. Having a compromised immune system, I pick up infections very easily. As Jin said all those years ago, that this would be as good as it gets, so I have to accept this as par for the course.

Despite going to Slimming World for about nineteen to twenty months, prior to my son Paul's wedding, I only managed to lose one stone (fourteen pounds). Having an under-active thyroid made it almost impossible to lose weight on a regular basis, and as the big day drew near, I was very disheartened at such a measly weight loss.

After losing Timmy to an inoperable heart problem, Billy followed with a tumour in his abdomen, leaving me with just Ollie and Sam. Ollie was run over and killed in July 2013. He was just a few weeks off his eleventh birthday, and I plummeted into the depths of grief. I had just started editing the manuscript of his diaries, which first appeared on my website, thinking I would try to get them published. Each month, after Ollie's Diaries appeared on my website, people wrote telling me how much they'd enjoyed them, how funny they were. They were a true reflection of Ollie's character and personality.

I put the manuscript away in a drawer. I couldn't look at it, because the diaries were so full of Ollie's adventures and his zest for life, that it was too painful to read. One of my subscribers in America suggested that Ollie continued his diaries from Rainbow Bridge. At the time, coming as it did only a day after Ollie's death, I thought that was a very tacky idea, although I didn't say anything to her. That night, though, while in bed trying to sleep, a small germ of an idea began to take root and I had to get up, switch the computer on and after about an hour of frantic, furious typing, I had the bones of an idea ready. I worked on it over the next few months, taking a notebook with me on holiday to Cape Verde in September, and I carried on writing a chapter a day, typing them up when I got back home.

Sam was almost seventeen years old, and he had kidney disease. A tumour above his right eye appeared when we got back from Cape Verde, which the vet monitored. It worsened over the Christmas period and, sadly, he had to be put to sleep on 2 January 2014. In less than six months I had lost two beautiful cats.

Before Ollie died, he alerted me to a little tabby stray that had pitched up on the decking, outside the back door. This was September/October time of 2012. I thought the cat was very pretty, so I started calling her 'Maisie', although I have no idea why I would call a cat by that name. Every time Maisie turned up outside, Ollie would look at me, then look at the cat flap, and I knew I had to give Maisie some dinner. Ollie would then, once Maisie had eaten, go outside and they'd rub noses in greeting. Often, they would lie on the decking in the October sunshine. This carried on throughout the winter months, when we had a lot of snow, but Maisie never tried to come inside although I often tried to encourage her.

One Sunday morning in February 2013, when I got up, she was in the bathroom huddled by the radiator. She let me stroke her, and I spoke gently and quietly to her so as not to startle her. She stayed in the bathroom most of the day and I gave her meals in there. When I used the bathroom throughout the day, I took the opportunity to talk to her and stroke her. I was hugely surprised, however, when she got up and walked into the lobby area, between the bathroom and the kitchen, and I noticed her 'accoutrements' at the back! Thinking quickly, I began to call him Casey, and this worked because it sounded like Maisie. It was also in recognition of our vet, Kevin, whose initials are 'K C'.

Casey moved in. I had him neutered and microchipped and he settled in very smoothly with Sam and Ollie. Within a few months, though, Ollie was run over and Sam had to be put to sleep, so he became an only cat. He didn't seem to mind, seeing off other interlopers to the garden, so I assumed he wanted to be the only cat. Kevin thought that he was probably about two years old, so I gave him 21 June (the longest day) for his birthday.

About a year or so later, another little mackerel tabby cat, with almost identical markings to Casey, started coming into the house while Casey and I were watching television. This little chap was very skittish and ran away the second I moved. So, it took a very long time, and a lot of patience, to help him to realise that he wasn't going to be hurt in any way.

He's very frightened of feet and was always worried when I

wore a pair of black trainers. Whether he's been ill-treated or kicked by someone in the past, I don't know, but when I took him to Kevin to have him neutered, Kevin said that he, too, was about two years of age. This saddened me because Gibbs, as I'd named him after a character in NCIS, had been coming round for about twenty months – that meant he would have only been about four months old when he started looking around for a new home.

Both Gibbs and Casey are very happy here and, after having had ginger cats for nearly thirty years, I'm now enjoying my life with two mackerel tabby cats.

Thirteen years ago, my grandchildren were still young people, just in their early teens. Now two of them, Matthew and Demi, have both got children of their own. Demi had her son, Leo, in August 2014, and Matthew's girlfriend, Lacie, had baby Paisley in May 2016. When Demi told me that Leo had been born just a few weeks before my 64th birthday, I aged about a hundred years overnight. Being a Great Grandmother made me feel ancient, but I am well aware that I am very lucky to still be here, and to enjoy my time with my sons, my grandchildren, and now my great grandchildren.

It's a sobering thought - if my brother Tony hadn't been a tissue match, I wouldn't be here now. The initial search of the national and international bone marrow registers provided no matches for me. Thanks to my brother, and the skills of the doctors and nurses in both hospitals, I'm here, living my life to the fullest, with two new cats, and a new man – Lawrence – and great grandchildren.

It has felt, at times during these past few years, that life was happening to me, and I was just an unwilling participant. But everything happens for a reason. I was exactly in the right place where God intended me to be in order for him to perform a great miracle.

Who would have thought that my love of writing and my love of cats would lead to a website on cats? And who would have thought that of my hundreds of subscribers, many would have a faith system and offer prayers on my behalf? And that God, in his infinite Love and wisdom, put all these things together for such a time as this.

Notes and glossary of terms:

I mention the Footprints poem a couple of times. I discovered that there are at least three versions of this poem, but I have chosen the oldest, original one, as I believe this one to be the most widely known:

Footprints in the Sand

One night I dreamed I was walking along the beach with the Lord. Many scenes from my life flashed across the sky.

In each scene, I noticed footprints in the sand. Sometimes, there were two sets of footprints, other times there was only one.

This bothered me because I noticed that, during the low periods of my life, when I was suffering from anguish, sorrow or defeat, I could see only one set of footprints, so I said to the Lord:

'You promised me, Lord, that if I followed you, you would walk with me always. But I have noticed that during the most trying periods of my life, there has only been one set of footprints in the sand. Why, when I needed you most, have you not been there for me?'

The Lord replied, 'The years when you have seen only one set of footprints, my child, is when I carried you.'

(Mary Stevenson, 1936)

www.freecycle.org This is a world-wide organisation where you join a community, nearest to your address, and then advertise items that you want to get rid of, or ask for things that you want. No money exchanges hands, and it's a good way to recycle items that would have to be taken to landfill sites, and to help others get things they want as well.

Leukaemia Care is a national blood cancer support charity. www.leukaemiacare.org.uk

CMV: *Cytomegalovirus* is a common herpes virus. ... But the virus, which remains dormant in the body, can cause complications during pregnancy and for people with a weakened immune system. The virus spreads through bodily fluids, and it can be passed on from a pregnant mother to her unborn baby.

EBV: *Epstein-Barr* virus (*EBV*), also known as human herpesvirus 4, is a member of the herpes virus family. It is one of the most common human viruses. *EBV* is found all over the world. ... *EBV* can cause infectious mononucleosis, also called mono, and other illnesses.

GVHD: Graft-versus-host disease (GVHD) is a common side effect of an allogeneic bone marrow transplant. An allogeneic transplant uses blood cells from a family member, unrelated donor or cord blood unit. GVHD can affect many different parts of the body including the skin, eyes, mouth, stomach, and intestines. GVHD occurs because of differences between the cells of your body and the donated cells. Your new immune system from the donor might see your body's cells as different and attack them. ME/CFS: Myalgic Encephalomyelitis/Chronic Fatigue Syndrome(ME/CFS) is a complex, multifaceted disorder characterised by extreme fatigue and a host of other symptoms that can worsen after physical or mental activity, but do not improve with rest. OBS: Regular measurement and documentation of physiological *observations* (i.e. clinical *observations*) are essential requirements for patient assessment and the recognition of clinical deterioration: this covers basic observations, including taking a pulse, checking blood pressure, measuring respiratory rate and taking a temperature.

More about Pauline

Pauline Dewberry had her first taste of fame, aged about ten and a half, when a poem she wrote was published in the Foyle's Children's Book Club monthly magazine. She trained to be an editor and had many articles published in teen girls' magazines at the time.

Marriage, two children, divorce, three house moves, many part time jobs later, but never losing her sense of humour, Pauline finally felt settled when Biggles and Garfield, the first of her many ginger cats, took up residence. Her website, www.thedailymews.com soon followed - as did more cats - and Pauline's life seemed complete.

One of her cats, Ollie, wrote his diaries, and when a tragic road accident claimed his life, he wrote a sequel from Rainbow Bridge. Pauline hopes to get these published in due course.

Pauline tries to live a healthy lifestyle, realising that getting a good night's sleep is of paramount importance, along with moderate exercise, and a sensible diet, low in sugar and fats.

She still enjoys writing articles for her website and has added a blog and a newspaper column (on cat care), as well as gathering up information for a book on pet bereavement.

Pauline and her blue-eyed, found late-in-life, soulmate, Lawrence, have enjoyed many happy holidays abroad together and hope to have many more – health issues permitting. They still enjoy visiting National Trust properties and have added English Heritage as well.

You can contact Pauline on pauline@thedailymews.com or p.dewberry@ntlworld.com